BRITISH LANDSCAPE PAINTING

Leger

OVER A CENTURY OF ART DEALING

BRITISH LANDSCAPE PAINTING

11th May – 2nd June

Monday – Friday, 9.00 – 5.30

THE LEGER GALLERIES

13 OLD BOND STREET · LONDON

1994

The pictures in this exhibition are part of our stock and are for sale. Some pictures that have recently been sold have generously been lent back for this exhibition by their new owners. Nos. 3 and 26 are not available for this exhibition, but reproductions will hang in their place.

———

Frontispiece: Detail, No. 1, Jan Siberechts

———

THE LEGER GALLERIES LTD

13 OLD BOND STREET

LONDON W1X 3DB

TELEPHONE: 071-629 3538 · FAX: 071-493 8681

If comment on any of the pictures in this exhibition is required, surely it must be on the great piece of topographical painting by Jan Siberechts. This is not only one of the masterpieces of the artist's maturity as a recorder of estates, but represents the most perfect and rare of early British views – fascinating in every passage – and amongst the finest of its genre of pictures that this firm has owned.

The canvas by John Wootton is one of the most beautiful and fluent landscapes by one of the earliest, most talented and various of the native born painters who can be said to have established an identifiable national school of painting. The other Hunting Piece by Ferneley, painted about a century later, marks a high point in the history of 'Sporting Art' and both pictures demonstrate their respective artist's understanding of the relationship between their patrons' love of sport and the country over which they hunted.

The further 'elevation' of landscape into 'history painting' is seen in the fascinating work by George Barret depicting the Royal Dukes of Cumberland and York inspecting the newly created Virginia Water in Windsor Great Park. A similar interest is also seen in the important pastoral by Thomas Jones, another recently rediscovered picture that anticipates some aspects of his work which was to become more obvious during his subsequent stay in Italy.

The more instinctive responses to nature are to be found in a small, but notable group of watercolours, which includes an intimate personal study by Paul Sandby, and moving, almost scientific, studies by Turner and Constable. Cozens' revolutionary treatment of landscape is represented by a wild and desolate Italian composition and Towne's more ordered view of landscape by three rather varied drawings. Of especial note, must be the beautiful and intense watercolour of Kensington Gardens by Linnell, a small and very rare masterwork of the early nineteenth century.

It is two years since our last Landscape Painting Exhibition and this catalogue includes some of the more interesting purchases which we have made in the intervening period. We are especially pleased that the new owners of a number of recently sold pictures have generously agreed to lend them back for this show.

David Posnett
Lowell Libson

If painters constantly apply themselves to the study of nature, as is reasonable to suppose; those who are employed in landskip-painting in England, ought to excel all others, as nothing can be so charming as the verdure of that country. And indeed many a painter makes a happy use of the delightful prospects which present themselves on every side. It is no wonder then that landskips are so much in taste, and that this branch of painting is as much cultivated as any other. There are few masters in this branch, much superior to those landskip painters, who now enjoy the first reputation in England.

André Roquet, *'The Present State of the Arts in England'*, 1755.

1

JAN SIBERECHTS

1627 – 1703

Sir Francis Pemberton's London Estate

An Extensive View of The Grove, Highgate
showing the demesne and gardens.

In the foreground the Pemberton family coach passes
before the house on a lane, and in the distance is seen the
panorama of Seventeenth Century London.
Among the landmarks are Westminster Abbey, Westminster Hall,
St. Margaret's, Goring House and Northumberland House.

Oil painting on canvas
Size: 42½ × 55 inches
Signed and dated 1696

Collections: Sir Francis Pemberton, (died 1697);
Anne, Lady Pemberton, widow of the above, (died 1731);
Francis Pemberton, son of the above;
T.M.Asterley, 1927;
John Sloane, (died 1971);
Mrs Cyrus Vance, daughter of the above, 1994.

Literature: T.H. Fokker, *'Jan Siberechts, Pêintre de la Paysanne Flamande'*, 1931, pp.98–9, repr. pl. 45;
Ellis Waterhouse, *'Painting in Britain 1530 to 1790'*, 1953, p.80;
Country Life, 22 January 1959, *Letter from Mary Vaughan*, p.152;
John Harris, *'The Artist and the Country House: A history of country house and garden view painting in Britain 1540–1870'*, 1979, pp. 47 & 73, repr. pl. 69.

This picture of The Grove at Highgate is one of the most notable examples of the Anglo-Netherlandish school of landscape painting which flourished in Britain during the second half of the seventeenth century. Although there had been earlier practitioners of the estate view including Danckerts, Wyck, Knyff and Griffier, as well as native born painters such as Streater, it was the arrival in England in 1673 of Jan Siberechts which lifted the genre to new heights of sophistication and as Sir Ellis Waterhouse was to comment he *'has better claims than anyone to the title of the "father of British landscape"'*. This view of The Grove is especially notable, not only for its beauty and quality, but for its considerable interest in recording, not a great house of the nobility, but the middling-size house of a successful and socially ambitious London lawyer.

When Jan Siberechts arrived in London at the invitation of George Villiers, 2nd Duke of Buckingham, he was at the age of forty-four a mature painter with a reputation established in Antwerp for Italianate style landscapes, and landscapes with a genre element such as groups of Rubensian peasant girls and carts and cattle passing through fords (fig. 1). Siberechts continued to paint such pictures during his early years in Britain, but soon found a ready market for topography. Bainbrigg Buckeridge writing before 1706 stated that

Siberechts *'did a great Number of those Pictures for him [Bucking-ham] at Cliveden House'* and *'after three or four years stay . . . left him and performed several Pieces for the nobility and gentry of England'*. Certainly he was working for the Duke and Duchess of Lauderdale by 1674 and Ham House appears in a large landscape of 1677 (fig. 2); however, Sir Thomas Thynne of Longleat House, on the evidence of surviving pictures, emerges as the major patron of his early years in England. It was in the three Longleat pictures, executed in 1675, 1676, and 1678 (fig. 3), that Siberechts found his true metier as a country house painter and in the following years he was to perfect the formula (as demonstrated in two of his masterpieces, the present work and his view of Wollaton Hall, Northamptonshire, figs 4 & 5) of establishing on canvas a house within its landscape whilst demonstrating its owner's status.

These views, which were invariably 'bird's eye' belong to a long tradition which had a clear precedent in Jan Brueghel's view of the Château de Mariemont painted in 1612. In England this device seems to have first come into currency with Hollar's well-known 1659 engraving of Windsor Castle, although there is an exceptionally early drawing of circa 1542 of Hull Manor House attributed to John Rogers, one of Henry VIII's surveyors of works. By the 1630s, when two magnificent drawings of the projected gardens at Wilton House were made, the idea of using a 'bird's eye' view was becoming the accepted form in which to convey a large quantity of architectural information in linear form. However, the earliest surviving painting of a 'bird's eye' view in Britain dates from 1662 when an unknown painter depicted Llanerch in Denbighshire (Yale Center for British Art) and in this canvas all the elements of the classic country house 'bird's eye' picture are included: house, gardens, figures of all degrees of status, cattle and the surrounding countryside. By the 1690s Siberechts had raised this genre to a level of harmonious sophistication which was to set a pattern for Wootton and the first generation of native born landscape painters of real importance.

Francis Pemberton, who commissioned the present portrait of his house, was born in 1625 at St Albans where his father was mayor. The Pembertons were of an old Lancashire family of some standing and Francis Pemberton's grandfather, Sir Goddard, settled in Hertfordshire in the early years of the seventeenth century. Pemberton was educated at St Albans

fig. 1
Jan Siberechts
The Flooded Road
Oil painting on canvas
27 × 39 inches
Formerly in the
Van Aalst collection

fig. 2
Jan Siberechts
Richmond Hill
Oil painting on canvas
92 × 144½ inches
Private collection

fig. 3
Jan Siberechts
Longleat House
Oil painting on canvas
Signed and dated 1678
48 × 67 inches

fig. 4
Jan Siberechts
Wollaton Hall
Oil painting on canvas
74½ × 53¼ inches
Yale Center for British Art
(Paul Mellon collection)

fig. 5
Jan Siberechts
Wollaton Hall
Oil painting on canvas
Signed and dated 1695
Private collection

Grammar School and Emmanuel College, Cambridge and was admitted as a student at the Inner Temple. Pemberton's pupilage was said to have been dissipated and as a result of his extravagance he spent some time imprisoned for debt in the Fleet Prison, where he continued his studies with such success that on his release he immediately embarked on a legal career of some brilliance. However, his stay in the Fleet appears to have had other compensations as Pemberton may have met his future wife there as a consequence of her father holding the position of Governor of the prison.

In 1675 he was made a Serjeant-at-Law in the House of Lords. Pemberton soon became entangled by the violent constitutional struggles then being enacted between the Houses of Lords and Commons and was eventually arrested by the Speaker and imprisoned in the Tower of London for a short period before Parliament was prorogued. After his release Pemberton was appointed King's Serjeant and knighted. Sir Francis served as a judge on the King's Bench during the 'Popish Plot' trials, but was considered to be too impartial; however, despite this, in 1681 he was advanced to Lord Chief Justice of the King's Bench and made a Privy Counsellor. In the struggles between the Crown and Parliament Pemberton was found to be wanting in zeal by the Crown and he was transferred from the King's Bench to the Court of the Common Pleas, a lesser court, before his removal from the bench altogether and the Privy Council in the autumn of 1683. After the 'bloodless' Revolution of 1688 (when William and Mary were installed on the throne), which he helped precipitate by his successful defence of the seven bishops, he once again fell foul of the House of Commons' interests and again was imprisoned.

Pemberton died at The Grove on 10th June 1697 and his remains were interred in the east end of the nave of Highgate chapel, a chapel of ease and the only licensed place of worship in Highgate, which adjoined his property though a grove of trees which he had planted. On the demolition of the chapel in 1833 Pemberton's monument was removed to Trumpington, near Cambridge, the manor of which he had purchased in 1675.

In 1677 Pemberton married Anne, eldest daughter of Sir Jeremy Whichcote of Cambridge, and Hendon Hall, Middlesex. His wife and seven children survived him, and were provided for by generous provisions in his will (Public Record Office: Prob 139/265), which left £4,000 to each of his unmarried children as a jointure or settlement and the residue of his estate to his eldest son, Francis. Lady Pemberton was left *all those jewels and the necklace of pearls which she hath used to wear . . . and all my plate and household goods and my coach and horses for her own use . . . my dear wife to take and enjoy all my lands in Milton Chesterton and Waterbeath in the county of Cambridge and my mansion house in Highgate during the term of her natural life.* Lady Pemberton died in 1731 and was also buried in Highgate Chapel. It was considered that Pemberton was a profound lawyer, deeply versed in records, yet of independent mind and for his age unusually honest. In addition, he appears from the evidence of his will to have been extremely successful, owning much property in Cambridge, Lincoln, Huntingdon, Southampton, Kent, Middlesex, the City of London and elsewhere.

In the sixteenth century it became increasingly fashionable for Londoners to acquire property in Highgate which was considered to be both attractive and healthy, whilst being only a short ride into the city, and some ambitious building projects took place in the 1550s. However, it was in the seventeenth century that grand houses multiplied and the village of Highgate attracted notable aristocratic residents including Thomas Howard, Earl of Arundel, the greatest collector of the period, who entertained James I, as well as Francis Bacon (who died there), at Arundel House, Highgate. In 1678 Sir Francis Pemberton purchased a property from Thomas Collett, replacing the old house with a fashionable new house, recorded in the present picture. Pemberton's other neighbours included the Earl of Kingston, and Lord Holles, two of the most influential men of the day.

Pemberton acquired additional property in 1683 and demolished Dorchester House which stood on the site before 1688 establishing what was to be designated on eighteenth century maps as the *Great Garden*, which is here seen in its immature state. It is no suprise that Pemberton should have constructed a garden of some importance around his house. Indeed, there were, according to John Beale in a letter to John Evelyn of 1659, other advantages than pure beauty in a garden: *'Scents given off by flowers and trees could ameliorate the air. Tis time for London to think of this, and to accept of a sweet and easy remedy agst ye corrosive smoake of their seacoale, yt cuts off more than halfe their dayes'.* Despite

the smoke that could be seen over London from the house, it was evidently an attractive enough view to merit Pemberton constructing two summer or banqueting houses, both with distant views of the city. Whether Pemberton took note of Evelyn's advice about the relationship that should exist between art and nature in a garden, we cannot be certain, but the planting of avenues, such as that leading up to the house from the road, and those to either side, are entirely typical for this middling-size house and estate. As Evelyn wrote in *'Sylvia'*, (1664), there should be a *'visible expression of man's imposition of order over nature'* thus reflecting both ownership and power. Whilst the gardens are nor neccessarily spectacular, they do encompass what John Rea called *'The Gardens of Delight, the Fruit-Garden and the Flower-Garden'.* The walks around the garden are clearly visible, with a profusion of espalier trees on the walls of the flower garden and planted flower borders around the fruit garden. Box hedges surround some of the trees and the vegetable garden has been incorporated into one corner of the fruit garden. To the right are seen the stables with accomodation for grooms over them, and to the rear of this yard, in white, is probably the laundry. John Harris (op. cit.) has pointed out that *'no other painting of the century records a vegetable and fruit garden so well'*

fig. 6
English School
Sir Francis Pemberton
Oil painting on canvas
50 × 40 inches
Private collection

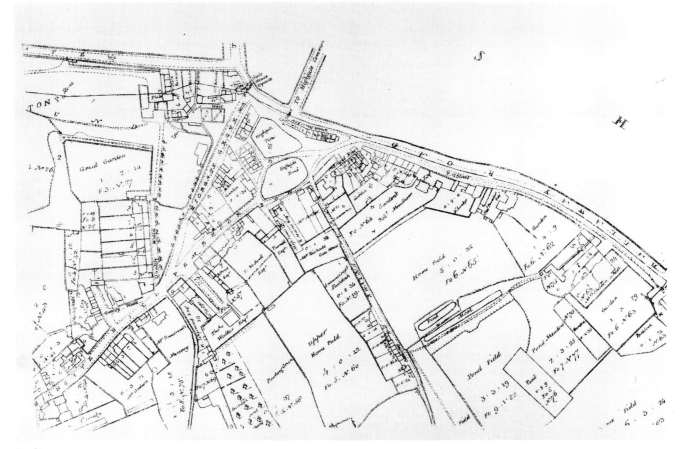

fig. 7
Highgate in 1804

Pemberton also acquired a row of semi-detached houses (now known as nos. 1–6 The Grove) which was known as late as the 1760s, as *Pemberton's Row*. These had been built by William Blake who had mortgaged the property to Pemberton. In 1706 Sir Francis Pemberton's trustees sold The Grove to Thomas Nicholl, who died the following year, and the property was acquired from his widow, Catherine, in 1733 by a London merchant Jacob Mendez da Costa. Da Costa's son, Isaac, sold the land to John Edwards in 1757 and it passed to his grand-daughter Mary Preston, who let it in the 1770s to Stephen Beckingham, selling the property in 1782 to Lt. General Charles Fitzroy, later Lord Southampton, who from 1832 broke-up the seventeenth century demesne as small building plots on 99 year leases which were later sold to the lessees on the death of the Rev. Thomas Coke Fitzroy in 1863. The house depicted in Siberechts' canvas stood on the site of what is now 7–12 The Grove and was demolished sometime before 1808, but appears clearly marked on a map of 1804. The houses in *Pemberton's Row*, later called *Quality Row* before its present name, *The Grove*, were sold in 1714 to John Schoppens before being acquired by his brother-in-law, John Edwards who, thus, was to own the entire Highgate property of the Pembertons.

fig. 8
Nos. 1 – 2, The Grove
Photograph
circa 1930

fig. 9
Nos. 1 – 6, The Grove
Photograph
circa 1930

(detail)

Northumberland House   Westminster Hall   Westminster Abbey   Goring House

St. Margaret's

2

JOHN WOOTTON

1683–1764

A Hunting Party in an extensive Landscape.
Badminton House is seen in the distance

Oil painting on canvas.
Size: 35 × 59½ inches
Painted in the 1720s

Collections: Duc de Chartres. Château Les Folies de Chartres,
sale, Paris, 28–29 November, 1834, lot 108;
Sir Robert Ashley;
Charles Romer Williams.

'No prospect of nature can awake more pleasing ideas in the imagination, than a landscape, distributed into verdant woods, and opening lawns, with the diversity of extended plains, flowery meadows, and clear streams; the heart of the contemplative beholder melts into secret raptures at this inchanting view, and he is immediately to hail the great benefactor who sheds such a profusion of beauties around him. But when he likewise regards them as so many rich magazines, intended for the accommodation of his table, as well as or the improvement of his health, and the solace of his mind, he begins to think it a reproach to him to be unacquainted with the manner of acquiring these enjoyments that were created for his use with so much liberality; and he is then convinced that Hunting, Fowling, Fishing, and Riding are more necessary to his welfare, than he might at first imagine'.

'The Sportsman's Dictionary; or the Country Gentleman's Companion in All Rural Recreations', Vol. I, 1735, p. 1.

For virtually the first half of the eighteenth century John Wootton was to be the most admired and successful of all the painters of landscapes and sporting subjects working in England, enjoying extensive patronage which, unusually for the period, was unaffected by the partisan political loyalties of the Whig and Tory landowners. Virtue noted that Wootton was *'well beloved by a great number of noblemen and gentleman'* and was in *'great Vogue & favour with many persons of ye greatest Quality'.* Indeed, Wootton who commanded the *'greatest price of any man in England'* understood the needs of his patrons who, in turn, appreciated his *'pleasant and engaging behaviour'* as well as his ability to paint landscapes, hunting pieces, racing subjects, Italianate capriccios, and portraits of both men, animals and houses (fig. 12). It was only with the rise in the late 1750s of Wilson, Stubbs and Gainsborough that Wootton's position as the foremost painter of landscapes and sporting subjects was to be eclipsed.

The present picture of a hunting party demonstrates Wootton's virtuosity both as a figure and landscape painter, and stands as one of the most beautiful examples of his work in this genre including both figures and animals executed in a most dashing and painterly manner within a landscape of remarkable freshness and directness of approach. In his literal treatment of landscape, albeit with a certain order imposed on it, Wootton could be said to have anticipated an interest in landscape which

was to be overshadowed for a large part of the century by the fashion of 'Italianising' or exaggerating 'picturesque' qualities.

Little is known of Wootton's early life and career. However, he was born at Snitterfield, a small village between Warwick and Stratford-on-Avon and there is a tradition that Wootton served as a page to Lady Anne Somerset, the daughter of the 1st Duke of Beaufort of Badminton, who lived at Snitterfield House between 1691 and 1710. It is likely that the successful start of his artistic career stems from the early encouragement and patronage of the Beaufort family (fig. 11) who were also major patrons of John Wyck, with whom Wootton was to study. Wootton made his early reputation as a painter of battle scenes and, as Arline Meyer has pointed out, his battle scenes *'relate both structurally and metaphorically to his paintings of the hunt. The aesthetic problem of presenting large numbers of men and horses in a landscape was similar; more significantly the hunt was viewed not merely as a sporting pastime but, like war, as a moral proving ground'* (Arline Meyer, *'John Wootton 1682–1764: Landscapes and sporting art in early Georgian England'*, 1984, exhibition catalogue).

In the 1720s Wootton responded to the stimulus of the old master pictures which were appearing both in the houses of his patrons and on the London art market as a result of the collecting activities of the British grand tourists. However, despite being seduced by the Italianising influences of Claude, Dughet and Poussin, Wootton remained, in essence, true to the traditions of the Anglo-Netherlandish view painters by producing landscapes which, whilst conforming to the ideals of the Augustan age, remained essentially works based on an acute observation and understanding of landscape.

The present picture contains most of the characteristic elements which Wootton used in the hunting pieces of his maturity (fig. 15), including groups of riders entering the landscape, almost as if entering onto a stage from the wings and a sweeping landscape of distant rocky hills and broad rivers as can also be seen in the influential set of four engravings by Bernard Baron (after Wootton, see fig. 14) of hare hunting subjects. The present work, although more broadly handled, shares certain similarities in its composition with the well-known picture of 'King William III Stag Hunting' (Private collection, fig. 13).

fig. 11
John Wootton
Staghunting at Badminton
Oil painting on canvas
Collection: The Duke of Beaufort
Badminton House

fig. 12
John Wootton
A Bay Racehorse and Groom
Oil painting on canvas
Signed and dated 1737
89½ × 139 inches
Private collection
(formerly Leger Galleries)

The house depicted appears to be Badminton, the seat of the Beaufort family who were to be Wootton's most constant patrons, and from the evidence of surviving letters it is clear that Wootton was on unusually close terms with the Beaufort family. The house is somewhat generalised in its delineation and situation, as was the artist's usual practice in subject pictures as opposed to house or estate views.

fig. 13
John Wootton
King William III Stag-hunting
Oil painting on canvas
Signed and dated 1729
50¼ × 60 inches
Private collection

Fig. 14
Bernard Baron (after Wootton)
The Chase
Engraving

The Chace   La Chasse

3

JOSEPH WRIGHT OF DERBY A.R.A.

1734–1797

An Idealised View of Vesuvius from Posillipo at Evening
with a Group of Ruins Clustered around a Tower,
seen by Moonlight.

Oil painting on (unlined) canvas
Size: 15 × 21 inches
Signed with initials
Inscribed on the original stretcher: '. . . Cathcart / Moonlight
Wright of Derby / the Hon. Emily Cathcart, Ascot Lodge,
Ascot, October 1893 / The Hon. George Cathcart.'
Painted in the late 1780s

Collections: Col. The Hon. Robert Fulke Greville (1751–1824);
Louisa, Countess of Mansfield (1758–1842), wife of
the above;
Hon. Sir George and Lady Cathcart (daughter and
son-in-law of the above);
The Hon. Emily Cathcart (daughter of the above),
1917;
George, 5th Earl Cathcart (d.1927);
Alan, 6th Earl Cathcart, to 1978;
Private collection 1992.

Literature: Benedict Nicholson, *'Joseph Wright of Derby: Painter of
Light'*, 1968, Vol.I, p.262.

fig. 16
Joseph Wright of Derby
Vesuvius from Posillipo
Pencil and wash
Private collection

Joseph Wright, born in Derby, was the first English painter of
importance to prefer living and working exclusively in the
provinces. Wright was also the first painter to explore in his
subject pictures the scientific interests of the Industrial Revolution and he counted many of the leading lights of the age,
including Wedgwood, Arkwright, and Erasmus Darwin amongst
his friends and patrons.

Wright was a pupil of Thomas Hudson, the portrait painter, in the 1750s and in the following decade became famous for his dramatic candlelit pictures, the most celebrated of which are *'The Orrery'* and *'An Experiment on a Bird in an Airpump'*. In 1774 and 1775 he was in Italy and on a visit to Naples, Wright witnessed an eruption of Vesuvius which was to become a favourite theme in his later pictures.

On his return from Italy he continued to paint portraits, although he increasingly became interested in landscapes with strong and dramatic natural effects as seen in the present work. This may have been inspired by the work of Vernet whose studio Wright would have been familiar with in Rome (fig. 18). Apart from a fifteen month stay in Bath on his return from Italy, he spent the majority of the second half of his career in Derby where he was a central figure in the vigorous intellectual life of the area. He was elected an A.R.A. in 1781, but when in 1784 he was elected to full membership of the Royal Academy he declined the honour, as by then he viewed the institution with some suspicion.

This beautiful and romantic landscape was inspired by Wright's own observations gathered during his visit to Italy and it seems likely that the present work is the one recorded in Wright's manuscript account book as a *small Vesuvius, a companion of the Lake of Geneva by Moonlight for Col. Greville* which was priced at 20 gns. The composition appears to be unique, unlike many of Wright's Italian landscapes which he often repeated on a number of occasions, and it is obviously an idealised evocation of Italy and based on a view of Vesuvius from Posillipo with the addition of the group of ruined buildings. The composition is perhaps closest to the drawing (fig. 16) of Vesuvius from Posillipo and the dramatic drawing in the Witt collection (fig. 17, Courtauld Institute, London) which because of its large size (13¾ × 26 inches) may be a compositional study for a painting such as the present one. An almost identical tower is found in a landscape of 1787, formerly in the Palmer-Morewood collection (fig. 19).

Robert Fulke Greville, almost certainly the original owner of the present landscape, was an amateur watercolourist and a patron of some note. Greville is especially remembered as the principal patron of John 'Warwick' Smith, the bulk of whose work he commissioned. Greville's elder brother, the Earl of Warwick, is

fig. 17
Joseph Wright of Derby
Study for a coastal view
Pen and ink and grey wash
13¾ × 26 inches
Courtauld Institute of Art
(Witt collection)

recorded as being the purchaser of Wright's *'A Boy Blowing a Bladder'* at Christie's in 1771. The present picture descended to Greville's widow, Louisa, Countess of Mansfield, a daughter of the 9th Baron Cathcart, who retained her first husband's title when she married Greville as her second husband. The picture then descended to her daughter and son-in-law who was also a nephew. The Hon. Emily Cathcart, a Maid of Honour and a Lady of the Bedchamber to Queen Victoria, died in 1917 when the picture passed to her nephew the 6th Earl of Cathcart.

fig. 18
Claude Joseph Vernet
Claire de Lune
Oil painting on canvas
Signed and dated 1781
34½ × 51½ inches
The Leger Galleries

fig. 19
Joseph Wright of Derby
A moonlit lake with castle
Oil painting on canvas
Signed and dated 1788
23 × 30 inches
Private collection

4

JOHN ROBERT COZENS

1752–1797

A View near Naples between Salerno and Eboli.

Watercolour
Size: 12 × 17⅞ inches
Painted circa 1784

Collections: With Palser, c. 1915;
Col. P.L.M. Wright;
Mrs. Cecil Keith, sister of the above, 1984;
Private collection.

Literature: C.F. Bell and T. Girtin, *'The Drawings and Sketches of John Robert Cozens'*, The Walpole Society, 1934–5, Vol.XXIII. p.64, under no.303;
Adrian Bury, *'Old English Watercolours and Drawings from the Collection of Mrs. Cecil Keith'*, The Old Watercolour Society Club, 1967, Vol.XLII. p.13.

Exhibited: Worthing, Art Gallery, *'English Watercolour Drawings from the Collection of Mrs. Cecil Keith'*, 1963, no.19;
Manchester, Whitworth Art Gallery, and London, Victoria and Albert Museum, *'Watercolours by John Robert Cozens'* 1971, no.66, repr. pl.65;
London, Messrs. Thomas Agnew, *'The Watercolour Collection formed by Mrs. Cecil Keith'*, 1984, no.65;
London, The Leger Galleries, *'English Watercolours'*, 1984, no.8.

fig. 20
John Robert Cozens
Between Salerno and Eboli
Pencil and grey wash
7½ × 10 inches
Inscribed and dated Nov. 8
Whitworth Art Gallery, Manchester

Cozens was the first major landscape painter to work exclusively in watercolour and his poetic landscapes occupy a unique place in the history of both British and European art when considered in connection with his predecessors and successors. Cozens, unlike his contemporaries, perceived the inherent

drama in the scenery which he studied and whilst he was content to depict, within reason what he actually saw, he was, however, selective in his subjects and compositions. In the majority of his works, Swiss or Italian subjects, any topographical content became a compositional device rather than the subject of the picture. The exact qualities that make Cozens' work so poetic are hard to define but perhaps the closest appreciation was made by the art historian A.J. Finberg earlier this century, *'their haunting beauty and incomparable power are spiritual, not material'*.

Cozens was to both anticipate and inspire Turner, Girtin and Constable. Turner and Girtin owed a direct debt to Cozens for they both spent a substantial part of their formative years copying Cozens' watercolours and many of the interests and compositional devices seen in their most sublime works demonstrate Cozens' great influence on them. Constable is known to have owned at least one watercolour by Cozens (fig. 21), who he stated *'was the greatest genius that ever touched landscape'*.

In May 1782 John Robert Cozens set out for Italy for the second time in the entourage of the eccentric millionaire and collector William Beckford who, at the age of nineteen, was making his third visit to the Continent, accompanied also by a tutor, cook, physician and a musician, as well as the usual valets and grooms. Beckford had been a pupil of John Robert's father, Alexander, and as early as 1780 had commissioned some drawings from John Robert.

The most complete record of the tour can be gathered from the seven surviving sketchbooks (Whitworth Art Gallery, Manchester) which Cozens used on these travels. The three carriages and outriders passed through Cologne and Augsburg before entering the Tyrol on 4th June when Cozens made the first drawing in his sketchbook. They passed rapidly through Rome and arrived in Naples on 6th July. At this time the party was staying with Sir William Hamilton and his first wife (not the famous Emma), and there Cozens, the musician Burton and Lady Hamilton fell ill. The subsequent deaths of Burton and especially that of Lady Hamilton upset Beckford who immediately returned to England, leaving Cozens to convalesce and to continue pursuing his commission for Beckford.

Cozens worked in the area around Naples until December when he revisited Rome before returning to England in September 1783. There is some evidence that Cozens showed his sketchbooks to Beckford at Geneva in November 1783 when the subjects of the finished watercolours might possibly have been chosen. On his return to England he worked on the watercolours which Beckford had commissioned.

This watercolour, which is based on a drawing made on 8th November, 1782 (Book IV, no.16 (fig. 20)), was evidently not made for Beckford and is known in no other version, and it was unknown to Bell and Girtin when they were compiling their catalogue which lists only the sketchbook drawing. It differs slightly from the sketch in omitting a group of trees which frames the right hand side of the composition. The present watercolour depicts the dramatic and rugged nature of the Italian scenery which is further highlighted by the emphasis which Cozens gives to the elemental nature of the subject. In this it may most closely be compared with the Victoria and Albert Museum's 'Between Brixen and Bolzano: Storm' (fig. 22).

fig. 21
John Robert Cozens
Eisak in the Tyrol
Watercolour
19¼ × 26¾ inches
Signed and dated 1791
Formerly in the collections of
Sir George Beaumont and John Constable
National Gallery of Canada, Ottawa

fig. 22
John Robert Cozens
Between Brixen and Bolzano
Watercolour
Victoria and Albert Museum

5

FRANCIS TOWNE

1740–1816

The Lake of Klontal, near Glarus, Switzerland

Pen and ink and grey washes
Watermark: Fleur-de-lis
Size: $11\frac{1}{4} \times 18\frac{3}{8}$ inches
Signed, inscribed, numbered and dated on the reverse: *'Lake of Clonthalee near Glaris / No 26. Sept 2nd 1781 light from the left hand in morning / Francis Towne'*

Collections: James White (d. 1825) by bequest from the artist, with reversion to;
John Herman Merivale, and by descent in the Merivale family, Barton Place, Exeter;
F.O. Roberts;
and by descent to 1993.

Exhibited: Possibly, London, 20 Lower Brook Street, *'A Series of the most picturesque scenes in the neighbourhood of Rome, Naples and other parts of Italy, Switzerland, etc., . . . The whole drawn on the spot by Francis Towne, Landscape Painter'*, 1805, nos. 100 or 108, (*Near Glaris*)

Francis Towne left Rome for England in August 1781, in the company of John 'Warwick' Smith (fig. 24). Despite the somewhat confusing dating of some of Towne's drawings at this time, he appears to have been at Lake Lugano on 24th August, visiting Lake Como a few days later, before heading north over the Splugen Pass to reach Wallenstadt by 1st September. Towne made the present drawing a day later during the four days which he spent sketching in the environs of the Canton of Glarus as he travelled via Lausanne to Geneva. A landscape similarly executed in pen and grey inks is in the Metropolitan Museum of Art, New York, and another in the collection of Birmingham Museums and Art Gallery (fig. 23). Towne exhibited two views *'near Glaris'* in his only public exhibition of his watercolours and drawings held in London in 1805; the present drawing may be one of the exhibited drawings, but as is usually the case with this particular exhibition it is difficult to precisely confirm the inclusion of any particular drawing.

This major drawing demonstrates the great powers of observation and analysis that are to be found in Towne's best work of the 1780s. Perhaps his finest works were executed in 1781 during his stay in Italy and on his return journey to England and Martin Hardie has noted that *'Towne's Swiss drawings are undoubtedly his finest work. Among the solitudes of the frozen Alps a new spirit seized him. His power of realising structure and simplifying mass found ideal scope in the superb mountain scenery, in the grandeur of vast rocky piles and slowly moving glaciers. His talents had by this time come to their full development. . . Among the Alps his vision is large and calm; his interpretation depends on his sense of appropriate and austere design; his colour is wisely subservient to form. In drawing he has the art of extracting symmetry and order from wild profusion. From endless shapes and contours of sky-line, ridge and scree, or rock and glacier, from infinite varieties of rich and changing colour, he chooses the immanent and eternal simplicities. He disregards the picturesque; he is less scenic even than Cozens. With unerring line he preserves the essential sublimity of mountain form'.* (Martin Hardie, *Water-colour Painting in Britain*, Vol. I, *The Eighteenth Century*, 1966, p.121).

In his drawings of this period, and this is especially so in the monochrome sheets, Towne appears to be grappling with the problems of understanding and conveying mass, form and

structure and these ambitious works are almost always precisely inscribed with place, time, date and lighting or weather conditions on the reverse. Other than a small group of large, and somewhat conventional, watercolours which he executed in the early 1790s for the Acland family, Towne seems to have made these revolutionary drawings entirely for his own interest and they do not appear to have been used as the basis for more conventionally finished studio works. Whilst Cozens subverted the eighteenth century tradition of topography by aiming to convey a sense of drama and place, Towne was also obviously fascinated by the scale of the scenery he was discovering, and sought to record it through what might almost be considered to be deconstruction.

Towne made three series of drawings during the month that he spent in Switzerland, amounting to seventy studies in all. Two sketchbooks (dismembered since at least the 1930s) were used concurrently, the smaller ($6\frac{1}{8} \times 8\frac{1}{2}$ inches) with drawings numbered from 16 to 59 and the larger ($11\frac{1}{4} \times 18\frac{1}{2}$ inches) containing drawings numbered to 29. There is another group of drawings dating from the end of the tour when Towne had reached Lausanne ($9\frac{3}{4} \times 12\frac{1}{2}$ inches) which are numbered to 11.

fig. 23
Francis Towne
Near Glarus
Pen and ink and grey wash
$11\frac{1}{4} \times 8\frac{1}{2}$ inches
Birmingham Museums and Art Gallery

fig. 24
John 'Warwick' Smith
Near Glarus
Watercolour
Birmingham Museums and Art Gallery

6

FRANCIS TOWNE

1740–1816

A Chestnut Tree near Rocca Del Papa

Pen and ink and grey washes
Size: 9¾ × 7⅞ inches
Signed, inscribed *'Near Roccha del papa / Wood of chestnut trees'*,
numbered 43 and dated 1781, on verso

Collections: James White (d. 1825) by bequest from the artist,
with reversion to;
John Herman Merivale, and by descent in the
Merivale family, Barton Place, Exeter.

This fluent study of a chestnut tree was made on the outskirts of
Rome in the Alban Hills above Lake Albano, a place of
pilgrimage for British visitors to Rome, to which city Towne had
travelled in 1780, joining there his friend William Pars. The
route from Rome would have been made along the ancient Via
Appia, surrounded on both sides by the remains of classical
monuments, tombs and villas. The two lakes of Albano and
Nemi had been formed in the craters of volcanoes and were
surrounded by wooded and often dramatic scenery, such as the
Galleria di Sopra, a favourite subject of Cozens'. Adrian Bury
has pointed out: *'With what creative excitement Towne entered into
the landscape in the Sabine and Alban Hills around Rome, choosing the
month of May when this neighbourhood is touched by the magic of
vernal luxuriance. Thanks to the constant practice and acute
observation the series of tree drawings done during that month show a
great advance on any previous work of the kind. . . . Having made a
preparatory drawing, Towne waited until the foreground tree was
caught in a brilliant light before applying his tints . . . two spontaneous
sketches Tivoli and Near Rocca del Papa, come into this series of fine tree
studies in light and shade'.*

In the time that Towne spent in the Alban Hills he was equally
happy studying the smaller scale aspects of landscape as well as
the more monumental prospects which revealed themselves at
every turn.

The majority of Towne's drawings from his stay in Rome
between 1780 and 1781, comprising seventy four drawings in
three volumes, were presented to the British Museum by his
executors, James White and John Merivale, *'in compliance with
the desire of the Artist, that his "Roman Drawings" should be deposited
with those of his friend Pars in the British Museum'.*

fig. 25
Francis Towne
Near Rocca del Papa
Pen and ink with wash
15⅞ × 10 inches
Signed, inscribed, dated 1781
and numbered 48
Birmingham Museums
and Art Gallery

fig. 26
Francis Towne
Near Rocca del Papa
Pen and ink and grey wash
$12\frac{1}{2} \times 8\frac{1}{2}$ inches
Signed, inscribed, dated 1781, and numbered 44
Formerly, Worsley collection

fig. 27
Francis Towne
Near Rocca del Papa
Pen and ink and grey wash
$15\frac{1}{4} \times 10$ inches
Signed, inscribed, dated 1781, and numbered 47
Private collection

FRANCIS TOWNE

1740–1816

A View on James White's Estate at Fordland;
trees in a rocky hollow with two figures looking down.

Watercolour
Size: $6\frac{7}{8} \times 15\frac{1}{2}$ inches on two joined sheets of paper
Painted circa 1790

Collection: Dr. Marc Fitch, 1987;
Private collection, 1993.

Exhibited: London, Leger Galleries, *'The Major English Water-colours and Drawings collected by Dr. Marc Fitch'*, 1988, no. 3, reproduced in colour.

This drawing, which is in a superb state of preservation, demonstrates Towne's ability to record with great refinement the structure and complexities of this wooded and rocky landscape. Towne's watercolours were made largely for his own interest and were primarily elaborate sketchbook studies which were often made up of a number of sheets of paper, usually taken from his sketchbooks. The present drawing, which is undated and unnumbered, was perhaps given to James White, the artist's closest friend and who was to be appointed his executor with a life interest in all of Towne's drawings. Certainly the style of the penwork in his drawing was obviously an influence on John White Abbott, the nephew of James White, who was not only to inherit his uncle's estate near Exeter (fig. 28), but was also a close friend, pupil, patron, and sketching companion of Towne.

Towne treats a subject which was a favourite one throughout his career, that of trees seen from below with a strong light source behind them. What is noticeable in the present watercolour, executed after both the Italian and Lake District tours of 1781

and 1786, is his ability to render the rock formations in a manner which is both economic in its use of a pen outline whilst communicating a large amount of highly detailed and convincing information. It is interesting to note that Towne in the present drawing has set out to make an analytical drawing of a local subject, much in the manner of his most challenging subjects which mostly derive from his two major tours. A parallel to his close look at the complexities of organic forms may be seen in Abbott's study of Rocks and Branches (no. 9) and of a tree (no. 11).

fig. 28
John White Abbott
Trees at Fordland
Pen and ink and wash
Inscribed and dated Sept. 1838
Private collection

JOHN WHITE ABBOTT

1763–1851

A View on the Dart at Holne Bridge

Watercolour
Size: 6⅝ × 4¹¹⁄₁₆ inches
Signed with initials, numbered 7, inscribed *'Holne Chase'* and
dated Augt. 30 1798 on the reverse of the original mount

Collections: Elizabeth Abbott, the artist's daughter;
Miss Rosamund Coldwell, a gift from the above;
Cuthbert Heath, by descent;
and by descent.

John White Abbott was born at Exeter where he was educated
and later practised as a surgeon and apothecary. Through his
uncle, James White (see no. 7), Abbott was to meet Sir Joshua
Reynolds, Sir George Beaumont, Benjamin West and perhaps
most importantly, Francis Towne, who could be said to be a
central figure in his life. Abbott was to become Towne's friend,
pupil and patron, and although he dedicated himself to the
pursuit of the study of landscape, exhibiting drawings regularly
at the Royal Academy as an Honorary Exhibitor to favourable
comment, he remained an amateur, never selling a picture,
content to practice his art for its own sake, whilst following his
calling as a surgeon. His work was almost entirely based on the
scenery of Devon, apart from one tour to Scotland and the
North of England in 1791, and unlike Towne, who seems to
have needed to be stretched by landscapes which he considered
to be more challenging, Abbott flourished in his native Devon,
and it would be fair to say that his best work is almost always
consistently more interesting and successful than the majority
of Towne's West Country landscapes. Abbott inherited his
uncle's estate, Fordlands, in 1825 and was obviously greatly
respected, being appointed Deputy Lieutenant of Devonshire
in 1831.

fig. 29
John White Abbott
The Dart from Holne Chase
Watercolour
5¾ × 6⅝ inches
Private collection
(formerly, Leger Galleries)

Abbott's best works executed in pen and ink with either
coloured washes or a monochromatic grey wash demonstrate a
strength of line and purpose, allied to a real understanding of
structure and form. Not only was he able to capture the scale of
his subjects, but the prevailing lighting conditions and the
inherent dramatic qualities of a particular view. Although
Abbott's 'stained drawings' are similar in technique to those of
Towne, a not unusual technique at the end of the eighteenth
century, his drawings not only reveal an individual artistic
personality, but also a slightly different method of handling his
materials which are often much more delicately treated.

This view was taken on the south east border of Dartmoor some
two and a half miles from the village of Holne. This is a
particularly beautiful example of one of Abbott's coloured
drawings and its demonstrates the great subtlety with which he
handles colour.

JOHN WHITE ABBOTT

1763–1851

A Study of Rocks and a Fallen Tree in a Wood

Pen and ink and grey washes
$7\frac{1}{2} \times 10\frac{3}{8}$ inches

Collections: Elizabeth Abbott, the artist's daughter;
Mrs. Rosamund Coldwell, a gift from the above;
Cuthbert Heath, by descent;
and by descent.

fig. 30
John White Abbott
Undergrowth at Chudleigh
Pencil and grey wash
$5\frac{3}{4} \times 8$ inches
Inscribed and dated Sept. 1798
Private collection

This beautiful drawing is a fine example of the type of analytical drawing that Abbott was to make from time to time. In his choice of subject matter and in the way he chose to approach the challenge of recording this detail from nature Abbott was obviously influenced by the example of Towne who, above all things, must have educated Abbott to take an almost scientific interest in the component parts of landscape. Not only has Abbott made an extremely successful record of a detail which obviously interested him, but has also had the imagination to make a pleasing composition of it.

39

JOHN WHITE ABBOTT

1763–1851

Sheer Cliffs above a Coastal Road

Pen and black ink and grey washes
Size: $10\frac{3}{8} \times 7\frac{1}{4}$ inches

Collections: Elizabeth Abbott, the artist's daughter;
Miss Rosamund Coldwell, a gift from the above;
Cuthbert Heath, by descent;
and by descent.

fig. 31
Francis Towne
Holincote, near Minehead
Pen and ink and grey wash
12 × 19 inches
Inscribed and dated 1785
Private collection

This sublime composition which may be, in part, a work of the imagination but based largely on elements of Devonshire scenery, demonstrates Abbott's ability to translate a grandeur of scale onto a small sheet. Throughout his long artistic career Abbott had the taste and ability to elegantly compose his pictures and the present example not only reveals his powerful sense of the dramatic, but the rare achievement in an artist who had not travelled on the Continent in successfully translating the immensity of a landscape in an economic way.

JOHN WHITE ABBOTT

1763–1851

A Study of a Tree in a Forest Clearing

Pencil, pen, ink and grey washes
Size: $17 \times 11\frac{5}{8}$ inches
Drawn in the mid to late 1790s

Collections: Elizabeth Abbott, the artist's daughter;
              Miss Rosamund Coldwell, a gift from the above;
              Cuthbert Heath, by descent;
              and by descent.

fig. 32
John White Abbott
Trees in Peamore Park
Watercolour
17 × 14 inches
Signed and dated 1799
Fitzwilliam Museum, Cambridge

This drawing of a tree is perhaps the artist's grandest monochrome drawing and is both a 'scientific' study and a composition of some considerable sophistication. Both Towne (see no. 6) and Abbott appear to have been fascinated by trees and they both had ample opportunity to study them in their native Devon. The recent exhibition, *'The Great Age of British Watercolours'*, seen in London and Washington, interestingly exhibited side by side virtually identical drawings of a group of trees made in 1799 and 1800 by Abbott and Towne respectively, demonstrating not only the similarity of their interests, but also the small, but characteristic differences in individual technique and approach. The present drawing once again reveals Abbott's ability to carry off a monumental composition of some complexity, whilst maintaining an economy in its achievement.

43

ROBERT ADAM F.R.S., F.S.A.

1728–1792

A Ruined Castle in an Idealised Landscape

Pen and ink and grey washes
With the *'Blair Adam'* mount
Size: $9\frac{5}{8} \times 12$ inches

Collections: Adam family collections, Blair Adam.

Robert Adam, the son of a successful architect and builder, William Adam, was educated in Edinburgh, and was already a competent artist by the age of fifteen. In 1754 he and his brother, James, went to Italy to complete their artistic training. Unlike most artists who studied in Italy at this period, the Adam brothers travelled as Grand Tourists *'as a gentleman would do for his pleasure'*. The Adam brothers were planning a career on a national scale rather than one based on their father's exclusively Scottish practise and to that aim Robert set about collecting the necessary credentials to enable him to establish himself as the leading arbiter of taste on his return to London. In Rome he studied under Clerisseau, Lallemand, Piranesi, and Batoni, also collecting and commissioning drawings by them for the decoration of the Adam brothers London offices.

Robert Adam pursued a serious interest in landscape throughout his career, indeed it was a significant factor in his success as an architect that he always conceived his buildings as part of an overall canvas. Adam knew Sandby from 1747 when the watercolourist was working for the Board of Ordnance on a survey of the Highlands and early drawings show him copying Sandby's compositions as well as those of Marco Ricci.

Adam was particularly interested in the 'picturesque' and his later landscape drawings shared many of the artistic ideals made popular by the Rev. William Gilpin in his illustrated Tours and

essays on the picturesque. A central component was to be the dramatically placed castle and from the mid 1770s Adam was to draw on the experience of some of his Scottish commissions in the creation, of what were described at the time, of his *'original inventions'*. Adam's idealised romantic Scottish landscapes almost always included a castle as the central subject of the composition and it usually followed a basic straggling design based, despite his antiquarian knowledge, on no particular historic example (fig. 33). Indeed, his Scottish compositions share much of the vocabulary of romantic literature of the period as demonstrated in Walpole's *'Castle of Otranto'* or Beckford's *'Vathek'*, and his artistic concerns are similar to those of Cozens; however, Adam's interest lies largely in the grandeur of the castle within the landscape, rather than in the grandeur of landscape with a castle as a cipher.

Adam's atmospheric drawings were greatly appreciated during his life and his obituary in the *Gentleman's Magazine* noted that his *'talents extended beyond the line of his own profession: he displayed in his numerous drawings in landscape a luxuriance of composition, and an effect of light and shadow, which have scarcely ever been equalled'*.

fig. 33
Robert Adam
A Castle
Pen and ink and wash
Henry E Huntington Library
and Art Gallery, San Marino

JOHN LAPORTE

1761–1839

An Idealised Landscaped with Elegant Rustic Figures

Bodycolour
Size: 8 × 10¾ inches

We have little information concerning Laporte's early life, but his family was of French origin and an inspection of his letters reveals that written English did not come naturally to him. There is some circumstantial evidence that he may have spent his first years in Dublin where there was a large Huguenot community and certainly his earliest known address in London was at the house of the artist John Melchior Barralet, who had previously come from Dublin. In any event Laporte exhibited from 1778 at the Royal Academy and for the next few years his pictures sent there mainly comprised views of London, Kent and Surrey. However, after 1790 he appears to have travelled more extensively, showing numerous watercolours of the Isle of Wight; the Lake district; Wales; Ireland; Italy and Switzerland. By 1800 James Roberts was able to write that Laporte's name and talents *'are so well known as to need no encomium'.*

One of Laporte's most important projects was his collaboration with William Frederick Wells in making soft-ground etchings for *'A Collection of Prints illustrative of English Scenery, from the drawings and Sketches of Thos. Gainsborough R.A.'* between 1802 and 1804. Laporte was also actively employed as a drawing master, and perhaps his most important pupil and patron was Dr Thomas Monro (see no. 25) who told Farington that he had purchased some £500 or £600 worth of Laporte's drawings. Laporte was also to combine his interests and skills as a drawing master and as a printmaker in the production of plates for drawing manuals such as *'A new Drawing Book in Different Coloured Chalks, for young practitioners in Landscape'* of 1809.

Laporte preferred to paint in bodycolour, and is one of the most sophisticated British practitioners in this medium, which was also used by Sandby and George Barret Snr. Seguier, writing in the nineteenth century, commented that *'his body-colour drawings are very masterly; he introduced a greater variety of tints in his foliage than old George Barret did, and his pencilling is also sharper and more decided'.*

fig. 34
John Laporte
Wanstead Grove
Bodycolour
10¼ × 15 inches
Pierpont Morgan Library, New York

14

PAUL SANDBY R.A.

1730–1809

A View of St. Martin's Court from a nearby house.
The trade sign of John Noble is prominently displayed, and a woman is seen at a second floor window.

Watercolour
Size: 7 × 8⅜ inches
Painted in the 1770s

This notable watercolour by Paul Sandby is an unusually intimate work, executed in the artist's most attractive manner of the 1770s. It is especially interesting as a record of how central London appeared in the mid-eighteenth century. The subject of this drawing is St Martin's Court, near Cranbourne Alley, between St Martin's Lane and what is now Charing Cross Road. This alley, which looped-back on itself, contained the premises of John Noble, who ran a circulating library at the sign of Dryden's Head and both a bust of Dryden and a legible trade sign are visible.

John Noble and his brother, Francis, who ran another circulating library at Otway's Head, by the gate of Grays Inn in Holborn, operated two of the four circulating libraries in London at this period, as well as being booksellers and publishers. Samuel Noble, presumably another brother, is recorded as a bookseller at Pope's Head in Carnaby Street. A little more is known regarding Francis Noble's activities, than those of his brother John, presumably due to the prominence of his premises. In the 1770s Francis published a catalogue of the contents of his circulating library numbering some twenty thousand volumes and, we can presume that John Noble was perhaps trading on a similar scale. James Boswell recorded in his Journal that *'Noble also sends me from time to time a fresh supply of novels from his circulating library'* despite having at a time of particular impecunity having *'recollected that I had left a guinea of security at Noble's circulating library. I went and told him that he should put confidence in me, so got it back.'*

The present watercolour may be directly compared with the view from the back of Paul Sandby's lodgings at Charlton, Kent, in the Royal Library, Windsor, (fig. 35), for its domestic character and similarity of technique. Another, more elaborate, treatment of a London street is the view of Beaufort Buildings in the Crace collection at the British Museum.

fig. 35
Paul Sandby
From the Back of Paul Sandby's
Lodgings at Charlton
Watercolour
18⅞ × 14½ inches
H.M. Queen Elizabeth II
Royal Library, Windsor Castle

49

15

CAPTAIN FRANCIS GROSE, F.S.A.

1731–1791

A View of The Corn Mill at Wandsworth.

Watercolour
Size: 8½ × 10½ inches
Inscribed on the reverse *'Mill at Wandsworth'* and dated 1772,
also inscribed *'Corn Mill/Wandsworth, Surrey'* on a fragment of
the original mount

Collection: Dudley Snelgrove, F.S.A., 1992.

Francis Grose was born in Greenford, Middlesex, the son of a
Swiss jeweller, best known for modelling George II's crown. He
was a noted amateur topographical draughtsman, but extrava-
gant living soon exhausted the fortune left to him by his father
and forced him to earn a living at Shipley's Drawing School.
From 1755 to 1763 he was Richmond Herald and afterwards
Adjutant to the Hampshire and Surrey Militias from which he
probably derived his honorary title of 'Captain'.

Grose made frequent sketching tours, often with his fellow
antiquary Thomas Pennant, as well as with the artists John
Nixon and Moses Griffith. He exhibited a number of architectural views at both the Royal Academy and the Society of
Artists where he was an honorary exhibitor. The fruits of his
tours were published as *'The Antiquities of England and Wales'*;
'The Antiquities of Scotland' and *'The Antiquities of Ireland'* between
1773 and his death.

Grose was always a large man and known to his contemporaries
as the *'Greatest Porter Drinker of the Age'*. He died suddenly in
Dublin and was buried at Drumcondra, where his tombstone
records that Grose, *'whilst in cheerful conversation with his friends,
expired in their arms without a sigh'*. The St. James's Evening
Newspaper pithily commented that *Death put an end to his Views
and Prospects'*.

Francis Grose lived for most of his life at Mulberry Cottage,
Wandsworth and the present watercolour depicts a view on the
River Wandle looking towards the Corn Mill standing to the east
of Wandsworth Parish Church and which stood until the mid-
nineteenth century. Wandsworth survived as a large village on
the outskirts of London until the mid-nineteenth century when
the scattered villas between it and the metropolis began to give
way to comprehensive development. In the late eighteenth
century the village comprised nearly seven hundred dwellings
with a total population of about four thousand five hundred.
The land was about equally divided between arable use and
pasture, with about two hundred acres being devoted to market
gardens. Wandsworth's proximity to London allied with its
position on the banks of a river contributed to the growth of
industry throughout the eighteenth century. Lysons, writing in
the 1790s recorded that: *'towards the end of the close of the last
century, when great numbers of French protestants fled from the
persecution . . . many of them settled at Wandsworth, where they
established a French church. Amongst these refugees was a considerable
number of hatters, who introduced their manufacture at this place and
carried it on with great success. . . . The art of dying cloth has been
practised at this place for more than a century. There are now two dyers
here. . . . There is also a maufactory here for bolting cloth; Mr Henckell's
Iron mills; Mr Gardiner's calico-printing manufactory, which is of
considerable extent, and employs about 250 hands; another of the same
kind, lately established by Messrs. Lawrence and Harris; Mr Rigby's
manufactory for printing Kerseymeres; Mr Dubble's manufactory for
whitening and pressing stuffs; Mr Were's linseed oil and white lead
mills; Mr Shepley's oil mills; Messrs. Gattey's vinegar works; and
Messrs. Bush and Co's distilleries: these several manufactures, exclusive
of Mr Gardiner's, employ about 250 hands'* (Rev. Daniel Lysons, *'The
Environs of London being an Historical Account of the Towns, Villages
and Hamlets within Twelve Miles of that Capital'*, 1792, Vol. I,
pp. 502).

16

ROBERT DIGHTON

1752–1814

A Prosperous Farmer Visiting his Property
and
A Pedlar Trudging Past a Farm

Watercolours
Size: each 6¼ × 10¼ inches
Both signed on the trimmed margins
Drawn before 1796

Collections: Henry Carington Bowles (d.1793);
and by family descent to 1953;
Jeffrey Rose, (purchased 1953) to 1978.

Dighton was born in London, and little is known of his early life before 1769 when he exhibited three drawings at the Society of Artists where he continued to show works on an annual basis until 1775 when he transferred his allegiance to the Royal Academy, submitting pictures until 1799. By 1774 he was advertising himself as a drawing master and he seems to have specialised during the early part of his career in producing, in watercolour, either single portraits or conversation pieces where the composition owed much to the example of Gawen Hamilton.

In 1781 Carington Bowles published his first mezzotint after Dighton and he remained almost the sole agent for Dighton's work until his own death in 1793. The humorous or satirical prints which Bowles produced have done little to enhance Dighton's reputation for they were crude and obscured the competence of Dighton's draughtsmanship and the laying in of the colour washes to be found in his best works. Indeed, by the mid-1790s Dighton, realising that the caricature mezzotints were giving way to the more rapid etching process and feeling that he needed to master the technique used so successfully by Rowlandson and Gilray, began to visit the British Museum Print Room, making copies of etchings, and stealing large numbers of prints which he sold to the London trade and collectors after removing any identifying marks. His major depredations were only discovered when the purchaser of Rembrandt's *Coach Landscape* (stolen by Dighton) took his new acquisition to the British Museum to compare it with their impression. Dighton escaped conviction for his crime by trying to replace the works which he had taken. By the end of the century Dighton was competent enough as an etcher to establish his own printing press at Spring Gardens where he produced humorous prints with his sons, Robert, Richard and Dennis.

The present pair of charmingly drawn and delicately coloured watercolours depict in a humorous vein, a farmyard, perhaps on the outskirts of London, (see no.15). Although they reveal how a late eighteenth century farm looked, they are essentially lighter-hearted than George Samuel's drawing (see no. 17) of a similar rural subject. These watercolours were originally part of a group of twelve drawings of rural life which were, no doubt, intended for engraving, but no prints based on them are, as yet, traced, however a similar series of illustrations entitled *Twelve Elegant and Humorous Prints of Rural Scenes, adorned with Comic Figures* were published in Dublin by William Allen.

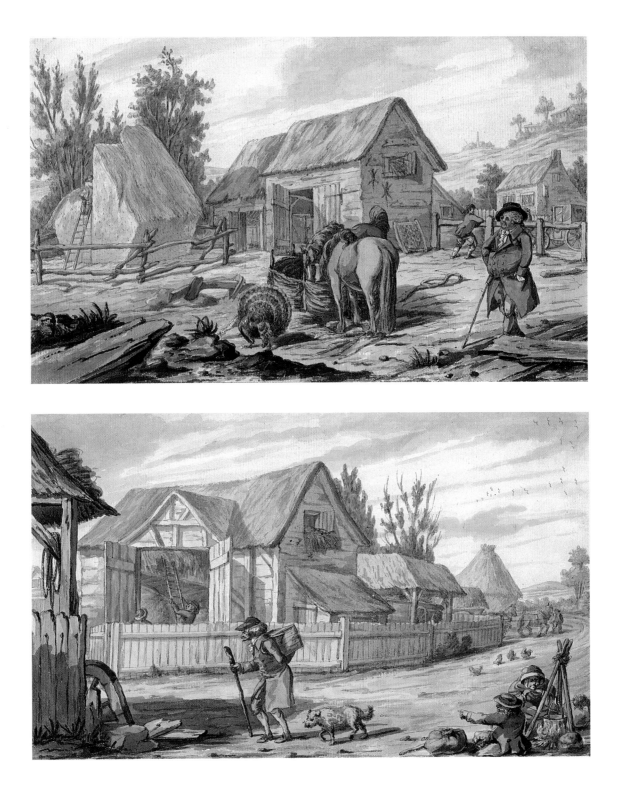

17

GEORGE SAMUEL

d. 1823

A Hovel at the edge of a Rural Road.
A woman is seen in the interior through the door,
whilst another woman sits outside smoking a pipe.

Watercolour
Size: $6\frac{3}{8} \times 9\frac{1}{2}$ inches

Very little is known regarding George Samuel's life or career, although it is obvious from the surviving evidence that he enjoyed a fair degree of success and recognition. Whilst he can only be regarded as a minor figure, his watercolours (or *stained drawings* as they would have been termed) are of considerable charm, and it is possible that his work was overlooked in the nineteenth century on account of his not having adapted to the more powerful use of watercolour which was being developed in the romantic period. The present watercolour is of considerable interest as it is an extremely rare example of a professional artist recording, in an age of picturesque sensibilities, the true appearance of a dwelling of the rural poor.

George Samuel exhibited landscape watercolours every year at the Royal Academy from 1785 until his death and the majority of his works fall into the category of picturesque topography with most of his subjects deriving from scenery in the south and west, with the occasional Welsh or Derbyshire view. However, among his exhibits titles such as 'Iron work at Ponty Pool' (1795) and 'A miner's cottage, Derbyshire' (1800), are perhaps indicative of an interest in a less conventional view of rural life. Samuel was among the founder members in 1799 of Girtin and Francia's Sketching Society, and he would appear to have been the oldest member of the group which at its inception also included Thomas Worthington (a pupil of Girtin); J.C. Denham (a friend of Constable); Thomas Underwood and Robert Ker Porter. Samuel met an untimely end when a wall collapsed on him.

The hovel depicted in this watercolour would seem to be a semi-permanent dwelling and it has been suggested that it may have been erected as a base for road-makers during the summer months. This is further supported not only by the encampment's proximity to a road of some type, but by the inclusion, adjacent to door of the hut, of what would appear to be some type of tool for tamping down a road surface.

fig. 37
George Samuel
A Picnic by a Weir
Watercolour
Victoria and Albert Museum

18

EDWARD DAYES

1763–1804

St. Paul's and Blackfriars Bridge from the River Thames

Watercolour
5½×8½ inches
Signed and dated 1791 on the original mount

Collections: Private collection, U.S.A., 1993.

Edward Dayes was perhaps the most refined and elegant of the topographers working in watercolour in the final years of the eighteenth century, and is certainly best known for being the early master of Girtin, (whom he treated unfairly in a vitriolic biographical sketch published after both artists' deaths) and as a major influence on the work of the young Turner, much of whose work of circa 1795 to 1798 is almost indistinguishable from that of Dayes'.

Dayes became a student at the Royal Academy Schools in 1780 and exhibited watercolours of landscapes, architecture and some ambitious figure subjects at the Royal Academy from 1786, and was much in demand by publishers to whom he supplied drawings for engraving, the best known of these being the designs used in Walker's *Copper Plate Magazine*. A similar view of the Thames was engraved by J. Walker in 1796 for *'The Itinerant'*, (fig. 38).

This London view exemplifies all the most attractive qualities that are to be found in Dayes' work: deft pen-work with no mechanical quality to the drawing of the architecture and a delicacy in the laying-in of the limited palette of colour which is combined with an elegance of design.

London's third bridge at Blackfriars took nine years to build, and was opened in 1769. It was designed by Robert Mylne, a Scot, who won the competition to select the architect whilst he was still unknown and in his mid-twenties. It was originally called Pitt Bridge, in honour of the Earl of Chatham, the former Prime Minister. At first a toll of a halfpenny (one penny on Sundays) was levied and this led to rioting, and the tariff was removed after the toll house was burned down in 1780.

fig. 38
J. Walker
(after Edward Dayes)
Blackfriars Bridge
Engraving
Published 1796

19

THOMAS JONES

1742–1803

A View of John Milton's Cottage at Chalfont St. Giles
with Harvesters and a Dog by Corn Stooks in the Foreground.

Oil painting on canvas
Size; 16¾ × 20 inches
Signed and dated 1774

Collections: Dr. Benjamin Bates (c.1736–1828).

Literature: A.P. Oppé (editor), *'The Memoirs of Thomas Jones'*, The Walpole Society, 1951, Vol. XXXII, pp. 33–35; John Sunderland, *'John Hamilton Mortimer: His Life and Works'*, The Walpole Society. 1988, Vol. LII, pp. 47,90.
To be included in Judy Egerton's forthcoming catalogue, *'The Works of Thomas Jones'* due to be published by The Walpole Society.

Exhibited: London, Society of Artists, 1775, no. 119 (*'A View of the House in Chaffant St. Gile's Bucks, where Milton resided during the Plague of London and where he wrote his L'Allegro'*).

The figures painted by John Hamilton Mortimer (1741–79)

Thomas Jones is considered to be one of the most important British landscape painters and his reputation largely rests on the small group of *'plein air'* studies, executed in oils, made in Naples between 1778 and 1783 which in their purity of execution and integrity of observation anticipate the studies from nature of the nineteenth century Romantic and Impressionist movements. However, the re-emergence of the present picture, unknown to scholars and last seen in public in 1775, demonstrates perhaps for the first time, many of the artistic qualities which become apparent in the works dating from the artist's long stay in Italy.

This major rediscovery is not only the finest surviving pre-Italian work by Jones, but also his most important and well recorded landscape commission.

This view of Milton's house was commissioned by Dr. Benjamin Bates who was one of the most advanced patrons of the period, purchasing major works such as Joseph Wright of Derby's *'An Experiment on a Bird in the Air Pump'* (National Gallery) and his first exhibited picture the *'Three Persons Viewing the Gladiator by Candle-light'*. Bates was a Buckinghamshire figure of some significance although he was born in the north. In about 1758 he settled at Aylesbury and later at Little Missenden, practising as a physician, and on intimate terms with the leading county families, as well as being a member of the notorious 'Hell-Fire Club'. Bates also actively patronised John Hamilton Mortimer, a close friend (who was to be buried in the church at Little Missenden), purchasing *'St. Paul Preaching to the Ancient Britons'*, which he later gave to High Wycombe Church, and the series of four paintings of 1774 *'The Progress of Vice'*.

Mortimer was also to execute the figures in the present picture and its pendant. The present landscape (and its pendant, now lost) is the last documented example of a long series of collaborations between the two artists which certainly date back to the 1760s. Mortimer, who was a portrait painter by training and a history painter and draughtsman by profession, was well known as being a frequent collaborator with his fellow artists of the Society of Artists in supplying figures for their landscapes

and subject pictures. A particularly fruitful relationship was held by Jones and Mortimer who were both members, along with Wright of Derby, of the Howdalian Society, an informal club deriving its membership from the Society of Artists, and they were also frequent travelling companions. The first documentation of a professional relationship dates from May 1769 when Jones records that *'my friend Mortimer has introduced the Story of Dido and Aeneas'* into a large landscape which Jones had been commissioned to paint. There are frequent references to collaborations between Jones and Mortimer in contemporary records such as Jones' own memoirs and those of Farington, as well as the lists of exhibition pictures at the Society of Artists and at contemporary auctions. In September 1776 Jones visited Dr. Bates's house at Little Missenden where Mortimer was staying. It was to be their last meeting as Jones sailed for Italy two weeks afterwards and Mortimer died during his absence. John Hamilton Mortimer was the most sophisticated figure painter and draughtsman of his generation and his good-nature combined with the unusual gift of being able to include appropriate figures in other artists' compositions without discordant effects, as seen in the present work, kept him much in demand.

Thomas Jones, himself, gives the best account of the progress of the commission in his memoir (op. cit.) and it is worth quoting at length.

'August 1st (1774). I packed up a few painting utensils and went down by the Aylesbury Coach with my friend Dr. Bates to his house at Little Missenden in Buckingham Shire – My principal business on this Occasion was pleasure, but my Ostensible business was to paint for the Doctor a view of the house at Chalfont St. Giles, whither, according to tradition the Poet Milton retired during the Plague in London and where he wrote his L'Allegro and Il Penseros –

'On the 5th the Doctor took me in his chariot to pay a morning visit to Mr. Drake near Amersham...thence we proceeded to Chalfont St. Giles to make a Sketch of the Aforementioned house which at this time was occupied by a wheelwright – I immediately set to work, and as we had bought Provisions and Wine with us, about three o'clock, sat down to dinner in the same room in which we fondly imagined that Milton had so often dined – Here we indulged ourselves in the sweetest reveries, and Contemplated every old Beam, rafter and Peg with the greatest Veneration and Pleasure – On these very boards thought we, the great

Milton trod – On that very ceiling (for he was not at that period blind) 'The Poet's Eye in a fine frenzy rolled' and pitied those poor, frigid, flegmatic Philosophers who would not have felt the same Enthusiasm as our selves – on the same Occasion – I had not long retired to my Station again to proceed with my work but I herd the Doctor, over the second bottle, spouting with an elevated Voice, the L'Allegro and Il Penseroso to an old woman who was spinning in One Corner of the Parlour – I could not proceed – but shutting up my portfolio hurried into the house to join him, when we drank many a bumper to the immortal memory of that illustrious Bard –

'9th I went also on horseback, and finished my two sketches of Milton's house at Chalfont . . .

'October 4th . . . I have already mentioned that part of my Business here at this time was to make a View of Milton's house, as it was called, at Chalfont for the Doctor – this I executed in a Small Oval, and in which Our common friend Mortimer, was to introduce some Subject out of the L'Allegro – But the Dr. not thinking the work complete without a Companion, I searched the most Solitary places near Chalfont, but could find no Scene in this beautiful Country, suitable to the Subject of the il penseroso – so was obliged to paint an ideal one – more sequestered and wild – having finished this likewise, excepting the figures as above – I took leave of my host & his family, and on the 5th November sett off for London . . .

'21st January, 1775. Went down by the Aylesbury Coach to Dr. Bates's at Little Missenden again, where I found Mortimer who was at this time painting the figures in the two small ovals which I finished on my last visit to the Doctor's. After remaining there for ten days, returned to London with my friend Mortimer.'

A sketchbook (private collection), measuring $6\frac{1}{2} \times 11\frac{1}{4}$ inches and used by Jones between 1766 and 1774, contains a group of academic studies made from casts of sculpture and a number of views taken in London and its environs. This book, now partly broken-up, includes four drawings made on Jones's visit to Dr. Bates in August 1774 and of especial interest are two studies (figs. 39 and 40) which are directly related to the present picture. A detailed study of the house (p. 19 verso) is extensively inscribed and dated *'The House in which Milton resided during the Plague in London and where / he wrote the L'Allegro and Penseroso in the village of Chaffont St. Giles Bucks / 5 August'* and also inscribed with colour notes such as *'grey brick tiles'*, *'tinted wash grey'*, *'vine'* and *'apple tree'*. A view overlooking the village which served as the basis of the composition of the oil painting (p. 33 verso) is inscribed *'The House in which Milton resided during the Plague / in London'.*

fig. 39
Thomas Jones
Milton's house
Pencil
$6\frac{1}{2} \times 11\frac{1}{4}$ inches
Inscribed and annotated with colour notes
Private collection

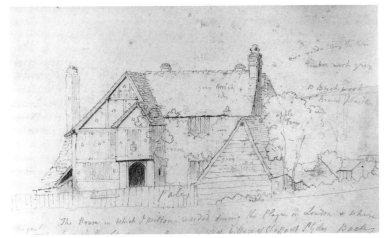

fig. 40
Thomas Jones
Milton's house
Pencil
$6\frac{1}{2} \times 11\frac{1}{4}$ inches
Inscribed
Private collection

20

WILLIAM MARLOW

1740–1813

A View on the River Saône at Lyon with the Château Pierre Encise

Watercolour
13¾ × 21¼ inches
Signed
Painted circa 1770

Collections: The Pendarves Family, Cornwall;
and thence by descent to 1993.

Exhibited: Possibly, London, Society of Artists, 1773, no. 182,
(*A View of the Soan; a drawing*).

William Marlow was born in Southwark in London in the same year as Francis Towne, and became a pupil of Samuel Scott, the marine painter, in about 1756, studying with him for about five years and also taking tuition at the St. Martin's Lane Academy. Influenced by Scott and the works of Canaletto, Marlow followed the calling of a topographical painter working in both oils and watercolours and his views of London and the Thames became well-known at the exhibitions of the Society of Artists Exhibitions of which he was a notable supporter, showing one hundred and twenty five works, compared to twenty five at the Royal Academy, where he had been invited to become a foundation member.

In 1765 Marlow left England and for three years travelled on the Continent, spending most of his time in Italy where, like many other English artists of his period, he was greatly influenced by the scenery and lighting which he saw there. On his return to England in 1768 he settled in lodgings in Newport Street, then the centre of artistic life, and started to exhibit continental subjects mainly of Italy and France, and from the annual appearance of these pictures at the Society of Artists and at the

Royal Academy one can surmise that Marlow's English patrons were eager to acquire them. In about 1788 Marlow went to live at Twickenham with a man called Curtis, whose wife Marlow had met at Vauxhall Gardens: Farington was to note in his diary that in 1808 there were six or seven children at the Twickenham establishment, *'some of them very like Marlow'*. Marlow's obiturist noted that he had been responsible for executing the designs for the seals of the thirteen original states comprising the United States. At the time of his death Marlow, who had long retired from painting, had an income of £100 per annum and amused himself making telescopes and other instruments.

The subject of the present watercolour, the Château of Pierre Encise at Lyon, appears to have been a particular favourite as there exist a number of versions executed in oil as well as watercolour, and this may well be accounted for by the fact that most British Grand Tourists heading for Italy would travel from Paris to Chalon-sur-Saône where they would embark on the *diligence par eau* for a pleasant two day trip on the Saône to Lyons where good accomodation could be had for 2s 6d a night. In 1765 Sir William Farrington found *'the situation wonderfully romantick, tis a most beautiful and noble city'*, and whilst there visited the factory making gold and silver wire.

Although Marlow exhibited at least six views of Lyon at the Society of Artists and the Royal Academy between 1769 and 1794, only his 1773 exhibit is specified as a drawing and the quality of the present work would suggest that it may be Marlow's 1773 exhibition piece. There are two other versions of the subject in watercolour, one of which was in the collection of both T.C. Girtin and Gilbert Davis. However, each of them is inferior in handling to the present drawing which also survives in exceptional condition.

21

GEORGE BARRET SNR., R.A.

c. 1730–1784

The Royal Dukes of Cumberland and York driving in a Phaeton
in Windsor Great Park. The Chinese Barge is seen on Virginia Water
and deer are grazing in the foreground.

Oil painting on canvas
Size: 41 × 54 inches
Painted circa 1765

Collections: George Keppel, 3rd Earl of Albemarle, (1724–72);
possibly, John Julius Angerstein;
William Angerstein, son of the above, to 1883;
Angerstein sale, Christies, 24th February, 1883, Lot
263, (purchased by Vokins, 185 gns.);
Baroness Burdett-Coutts, (Inv. no. 1107), d. 1906;
William Ashmead Burdett-Coutts (Bartlett) d. 1921;
Seabury Burdett-Coutts; and by descent to 1994.

Literature: Walter G. Strickland, *'A Dictionary of Irish artists',*
1913, Vol. I, p. 32;
A. P. Oppé, *'The Drawings of Paul and Thomas Sandby
in the Collection of His Majesty the King at Windsor
Castle',* 1947, pp. 79–80;
Oliver Millar, *'The Later Georgian Pictures in the
Collection of Her Majesty the Queen',* 1969, Vol. I,
p. 47.

*'It would be, however, unpardonable to pass over the merits of our
countrymen Gainsborough and Barret . . . the former for lightness of
handling, elegant rusticity of figures, breadth of chiaro-oscuro, and
sweet silvery tone of colour, is highly worthy of attention; while the latter,
for the character of a tree, and the true tone of grey distance, is highly
estimable. The three great names of Wilson, Gainsborough, and Barret,
form a school for the student, while their labours reflect the highest
honour on our nation.'*
Edward Dayes, *'The Works of the late Edward Dayes: Essays on
Painting',* 1805, p. 195.

This magnificent work is one of the most historically important landscapes of Barret's English career, and was originally a pendant to the famous canvas of *'The Duke of Cumberland visiting his stud in Windsor Great Park'* by William Marlow and Sawrey Gilpin (fig. 41, Collection, H.M. Queen Elizabeth II, Windsor Castle) which was purchased on behalf of Queen Victoria at the Angerstein sale in 1883.

The earliest recorded owner of both pictures was George Keppel, 3rd Earl of Albemarle (fig. 44), an extremely close confidant of the Duke of Cumberland, brother of George III. It is possible that both the present picture and the one in the Royal Collection may have been commissioned by Cumberland and given to Keppel, in whose arms the Duke died. The Angerstein sale of 1883 also contained a number of Gilpin's ambitious horse 'history' pictures based on Gulliver's tales which also came from Lord Albemarle's collection, and these too may have originally been painted for the artist's principal patron, the Duke of Cumberland.

This landscape contains the finely executed portraits of the Royal Dukes of Cumberland and York riding in a phaeton. Barret was in the habit of collaborating with his fellow artists and, although Sawrey Gilpin almost certainly contributed the deer seen in the present work, it is likely that Barret turned to Richard Cosway to execute the two accurate small-scale portraits seen here. H.R.H. William Augustus, 3rd Duke of Cumberland (1721–1765), the second son of King George II

and Queen Caroline, enjoyed a long and distinguished military career, being wounded at the battle of Dettingen in 1743, and was in command at the well fought, but unsuccessful battle of Fontenoy, and also at Culloden, where as a result of his ruthlessness in suppressing the Jacobites he gained the sobriquet of 'The Butcher'. He resigned all his military commands after making peace with the French in 1757, a treaty considered very humiliating to the King, his father. H.R.H. Edward Augustus, 10th Duke of York (1738–1767), the son of Frederick, Prince of Wales the elder brother of George III, entered the Navy as a midshipman in 1758 serving under Lord Howe, before being made a Rear Admiral in 1761 and an Admiral of the Blue in 1766.

This picture is an important commemoration of Cumberland's most notable non-military achievement, that of his improvements to Windsor Great Park and, especially, his creation of Virginia Water: whilst its very early possession by Keppel certainly celebrates his very close connections with the Royal Household.

The Great Park was looked after by a Ranger, who usually had a house in the park and enjoyed considerable privileges, especially when the monarch was not in residence. Although the Park had benefited from a certain amount of tree planting during Queen Anne's reign at the instigation of the then Ranger, the formidable Sarah, Duchess of Marlborough, the Great Park was essentially for hunting and the preservation of game was the primary role of the Ranger. William, Duke of Cumberland was appointed Ranger in 1746 (being succeeded by his nephew, the Duke of York, in 1766) and after his return from Holland on the Declaration of Peace in 1748, influenced by contemporary interest in landscape gardening, and prompted by a desire to employ as many demobilised troops as possible, he set about beautifying the park and much of the planting dates from this time. Popular opinion at the time was expressed by the lines:

> *Since the Duke's victorious blows*
> *The lily, thistle and the rose*
> *All droop and fade, all die away;*
> *Sweet William only rules the day.*

The Duke wanted to create a secret paradise of glades, woodland, lakes and eye-catching buildings and within weeks of taking up residence had, according to Walpole, *'disgusted the neighbourhood by excluding them from most of the benefits of the park'*.

Cumberland's most spectacular project was the creation of Virginia Water in about 1750 with the help of the architect, Henry Flitcroft, and Thomas Sandby, the Deputy Ranger and future Royal Academician. The name 'Virginia Water' dates from the time of James I's drainage projects of 1623–4 when he attempted to improve the marshy land around the *'Virginia River'*. Virginia Water started out as comparatively narrow pond, but by enlarging a natural basin, diverting several rivulets and damming their outflow, a considerable lake was formed, the apparent size of which was enhanced by judicious planting. The Duke had a barge, the Mandarin, decorated in the Chinese style *'as rich and gay as carving, gilding and Japanning can make it'*, which he moored on the lake (figs. 42 & 43).

fig. 41
Sawrey Gilpin and William Marlow
The Duke of Cumberland Visiting his Stud
Oil painting on canvas
41 × 54 inches
H.M. Queen Elizabeth II
Windsor Castle

fig. 42
Thomas Sandby
George II and the Duke of Cumberland
inspecting Virginia Water
Watercolour
$17\frac{7}{8} \times 29\frac{3}{4}$ inches
Subject engraved by 1754
British Museum

fig. 43
Paul Sandby
The Chinese Junk
Pencil
$4\frac{1}{2} \times 5\frac{5}{8}$ inches
Inscribed
H.M. Queen Elizabeth II
Royal Library, Windsor Castle

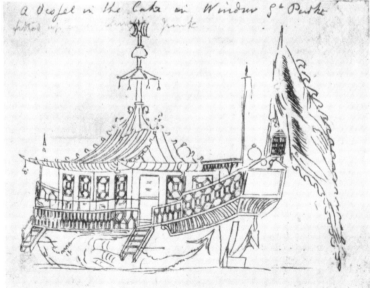

fig. 44
Sawrey Gilpin
The 3rd Earl of Albemarle out
shooting with his son
Oil painting on canvas
Private collection

George Barret is the best known Irish landscape painter of the eighteenth century and enjoyed great success during his own lifetime. He was born in Dublin in either 1728 or 1732, the son of a clothier, and was originally apprenticed to a stay-maker; despite this, he coloured prints for the Dublin print-seller, Thomas Sillcock, before gaining entry to the Dublin Society's School whose charter stated, *'Since a good spirit shows itself for drawing and designing, which is the background of painting and so useful in manufactures, it is intended to erect a little academy or school of drawing and painting, from whence some geniuses may arise to the benefit and honour of this Kingdom'*. The Dublin Society had taken over the drawing school founded by Robert West some years earlier and there from 1747 Barret studied under Robert West and James Mannin. Whilst Barret's earliest paintings in oils date from the late 1740s and are somewhat stiff, by 1755 he had executed a most beautiful Italianate landscape, which owed much to the example of Zuccarelli.

In the 1750s Barret appears to have been influenced by the ideas then being propounded by Edmund Burke, at Trinity College, Dublin, which were to take a final form in his *'Philosophical Enquiry into the Origin of our Ideas of the Sublime and Beautiful'*, (1757), and his interests changed to romantic scenery, and the study of landscapes from nature. It is said that Burke introduced Barret to Lord Powerscourt (although this may not have been necessary as the young artist was becoming well-known in Dublin) and throughout the first part of the 1760s he was to paint a series of views of the estate at Powerscourt which included some of the most beautiful and dramatic stretches of the River Dargle and the famous Powerscourt Falls. Barret went on to paint a set of landscapes for the Marquess of Rockingham, to whom Burke was then secretary.

In late 1762 or early 1763 Barret moved to London, exhibiting there four landscapes including two of Powerscourt at the Free Society and the Society of Artists in 1764, and winning the First Premium for the best landscape at the Free Society. The painter James Barry who saw the winning picture said that he had *'seen nothing to match it'* and compared Claude's work to it, unfavourably, as he considered that Barret's skies were superior. Barret went on to visit North Wales, which Paul Sandby had just begun to make popular as a subject for landscape painters, but he was also beginning to make a name for himself as a painter of noblemen's parks, as Edmund Burke noted in 1767: *'Barret is fallen into the painting of views. It is the most called for; and the most lucrative part of his business. He is a wonderful observer of the accidents of nature'*.

Commissions of the 1760s and 1770s included views of the park at Welbeck for the Duke of Portland; a number of estate views (fig. 45) for the Duke of Buccleuch; Gatton Park for Sir George Colebrook; Burton Constable for William Constable; and views at Norbury Park for William Lock, and it would also now appear, either for the Duke of Cumberland or the Earl of Albemarle. Barret's critical success was further confirmed by his appointment in 1768 as a founder member of the Royal Academy where he was extremely active, although Burke noted that *'he has had the ill luck to quarrel with almost all his acquaintance amongst the artist, with Stubbs, Wright, and Hamilton; they are all at mortal war, and I fancy he does not stand very well even with West'*. However, Barret did maintain good relations with a number of the most prominent painters of the day including the animal painter

Sawrey Gilpin R.A., the portrait painter, Richard Cosway R.A., and the figure painter, Giovanni Battista Cipriani R.A., all of whom collaborated frequently with him by bringing their specialist skills to bear in detailed passages in his landscapes. The most famous example of this partnership of diverse skills was the mural (now lost) that Barret, along with Gilpin and Cipriani, painted with views of the Lake District for William Lock's dining room at Norbury Park in about 1780. It is said that Lock, a friend to many artists, and a steadfast patron to Barret during the latter part of his career, had paid the debts of the financially feckless artist who had been bankrupted in 1771 despite the fact that, as Dayes noted, *'he was in receipt of two thousand pounds a year'*. Barret continued to exhibit at the Royal Academy until 1782, at which time through the good offices of his long-standing friend Burke, he was rescued from immediate financial hardship by the gift of the lucrative post of Master Painter to the Chelsea Hospital.

fig. 45
George Barret Snr
Southwick Park
Oil painting on canvas
48½ × 58½ inches
Formerly: Borthwick-Norton collection

fig. 46
(Detail)

fig. 47
Reynolds
The Duke of Cumberland
(Detail)

fig. 48
Reynolds
The Duke of York
Formerly: Armstrong collection

22

GEORGE BARRET SNR., R.A.

c. 1730–1784

A Ruined Tower in a Rocky River Landscape.
Rustic figures and sheep are seen in the foreground
and farm buildings beyond.

Oil painting on canvas
Size: $28\frac{1}{2} \times 29\frac{3}{4}$ inches
Signed with initials
Painted in the 1760s

Collections: Miss N. Oswald Smith, 1948;
Private collection, U.S.A., 1993.

Literature: W.G. Constable, *'Richard Wilson'*, 1953, p.239, repr.
pl.154b.

George Barret possessed an ability to compose just what the British collector of the second half of the eighteenth century wanted in landscape, in this case combining a ruin, which is of a type which is recognisably British, with an idealised Italianate landscape, inspired by the works of Salvator Rosa, an artist greatly admired by connoisseurs for the drama and poetry which he introduced into his works. Barret was equally able to turn his hand to the painting of 'views'.

It was often noted that Barret was able to make an extremely lucrative living by painting, whereas Richard Wilson could not, despite having studied in Italy (unlike Barret). This difference was probably due to the fact that Wilson's landscapes, by and large, involved an emphasis on classical imagery: however, at that time British collectors were looking to Italian painters for 'elevating' landscapes and to the works of their own country-men for topography. Barret was able, as in this painting, to successfully bridge this gap by his avoidance of obviously classical motifs whilst involving the viewer in the drama of an Italian landscape.

fig. 49
George Barret Snr
Landscape with a ruined tower
Oil painting on canvas
$39\frac{1}{4} \times 49\frac{1}{4}$ inches
National Trust, Anglesea Abbey,
(Fairhaven collection)

23

THOMAS GAINSBOROUGH, R.A.

1727–1788

An open Landscape with a Herdsman Driving Cows and Sheep
down a slope by a copse of trees. A cottage is seen in the
middle distance and a range of hills beyond.

Oil painting on canvas
Size: 21½ × 29½ inches
Painted circa 1786

Collections: Joseph Smith, Shortgrove, Essex (1757–1822) by
 1814;
 Joseph Smith (1845–1936) by descent, to 1889;
 Sir Edward Guinness (later 1st Earl of Iveagh)
 purchased from the above, to 1927;
 Hon. Alfred E. Guinness, by descent, to 1953;
 Maureen, Marchioness of Dufferin and Ava, daugh-
 ter of the above, to 1990;
 Private collection, 1994.

Literature: George W. Fulcher, 'The Life of Thomas Gains-
 borough', 1856, p.200;
 Ellis K. Waterhouse, 'Gainsborough', 1970, p.946;
 John Hayes, 'The Drawings of Thomas Gainsborough',
 1970, p.266;
 John Hayes, 'The Landscape Paintings of Thomas
 Gainsborough', Vol.II, 1982, 'Catalogue Raisonne',
 pp.558–9, no. 176, repr.

Exhibited: London, British Institution, 1814, no. 53, (lent by
 Joseph Smith);
 London, Whitechapel Art Gallery, 'Fine Art Exhibi-
 tion', 1890, no. 144.

This landscape, painted two or three years before his death in 1788, demonstrates the power, beauty and monumentality of Gainsborough's last pictures. It was in these years, as Reynolds eventually appreciated, that Gainsborough achieved a total and harmonious synthesis between the landscape of fact (as it might be called) and the landscape of the mind. These 'landscapes of sentiment' are amongst the most beautiful and important of European landscapes of their period and are now recognised as having been instrumental in forming a popular taste for the picturesque in late Georgian England.

In the late 1780s we find Gainsborough treating his favourite rural themes – themes that had preoccupied him from his earliest days in Suffolk – with a new broadness and confidence of manner, perhaps encouraged by the critical success that his landscapes had met with after the move to London in 1774. Walpole underlined Gainsborough's popularity amongst the cognoscenti by describing his Royal Academy exhibit of that year, 'The Watering Place' (National Gallery, London), 'as by far the finest landscape ever painted in England equal to the great masters'. Indeed, Gainsborough had been open to a number of potent influences in the years preceding the mid-1790s. An intensive study and appreciation of Rubens in the 1760s was followed by a fresh study of the work of Claude, Dughet, and Ruisdael and to use Reynolds's words 'what he thus learned, he applied to the originals of nature which he saw with his eyes; and imitated not in the manner of these masters, but in his own'. In his last works he appears also to have been influenced by Reynolds's Annual Discourses to the students of the Royal Academy Schools towards painting

in a somewhat 'higher' style. At the same time, however, his visit to the Lake District in 1783 seems to have confirmed in his own mind the rightness of his rather individual approach to landscape painting, although the scenery had little impact on his actual choice of subject matter.

The present canvas, painted at about the same time as his great statement of the period, *'The Market Cart'* (Tate Gallery, London), is a more intimate treatment of a theme that must always have reawakened memories of his earliest childhood in the wool town of Sudbury. Its handling and format can also be compared with another key picture of the period, the *'Wooded Upland Landscape with a drover and pack horses'* (fig. 51, Elvehjem Art Center, Madison, Wisconsin, formerly Leger Galleries) which when exhibited at his studio by Gainsborough was described by his champion Bate-Dudley as one of seven views *'the materials of which are in the utmost harmony of composition, and possessed of the highest touches of genius'*. In its treatment and exploration of the potential richness, variety of colour, texture and vigour of the brushwork it can also be compared with the handling of the landscape elements in the major 'mood' portraits of the 1780s such as those of *'Lady Bate-Dudley'* (fig. 50, Private Collection,) and *'Mrs Sheridan'* (National Gallery of Art, Washington) where Gainsborough could be said to anticipate the work of nineteenth-century masters such as Delacroix or Gericault. Gainsborough developed his treatment of light in his final years to an extraordinary degree of sophistication and this may be due in part to his experiments in painting glass transparencies for his light-box (Victoria and Albert Museum).

In the work of the mid-1780s we find a movement away from the powerful rhythmical landscapes of the 1770s and the early 1780s, a style perhaps best demonstrated in the 'Camden' drawing of circa 1783, to a more evocative and nervous treatment which heralded a growing sensitivity in the modulation of effects and a wider ranging power of expressiveness within a restricted though highly individual palette. Reynolds, his arch-rival and sometime fervent admirer, fully appreciated this, and with characteristic generosity praised Gainsborough's landscapes in Discourse XIV, delivered only a few months after Gainsborough's death and as such worth quoting at length: *'It is certain, that all those odd scratches and marks, which on a close examination, are so observable in Gainsborough's pictures, and which even to experienced painters appear rather the effect of accident than*

fig. 50
Thomas Gainsborough
Lady Bate-Dudley
Oil painting on canvas
87 × 57 inches
Private collection

fig. 51
Thomas Gainsborough
Wooded upland with drover
Oil painting on canvas
22¼ × 28¼ inches
Elvehjem Art Center, University
of Wisconsin

fig. 52
Thomas Gainsborough
Landscape with cattle and sheep
Drawing
10¼ × 12⅞ inches
Staatliche Museen, Berlin

design; this chaos, this uncouth and shapeless appearance, by a kind of magick, at a certain distance assumes form, and all these parts seem to drop into their proper places; so that we can hardly refuse acknowledging the full effect of diligence, under the appearance of chance and hasty negligence. That Gainsborough himself considered this peculiarity in his manner and the power it possesses of exciting surprise, as a beauty in his works, I think may be inferred from the eager desire which we know he always expressed, that his pictures, at the Exhibition, should be seen near, as well as at a distance'.

'The slightness which we see in his best works, cannot always be imputed to negligence. However they may appear to superficial observers, painters know very well that a steady attention to the general effect takes up more time, and is more laborious to the mind, than any mode of high finishing or smoothness, without such attention. His handling, the manner of leaving the colours, or in other words, the methods he used for producing the effect, had very much the appearance of the works and regular practice belonging to the art; but still, like a man of strong intuition and perception of what was required, he found out a way of his own to accomplish his purpose'.

The present painting is closely related to a drawing that is evidently a preliminary idea for this composition (fig. 52, Staatliche Museen, Berlin). The Berlin drawing, which closely resembles the mixed-media study of cattle of the early 1780s, differs from the painting in a number of details: in the finished picture an additional sheep has been included, the two rearmost cows have been replaced by a goat and a dog accompanies the drover. Elements of the landscape have also been changed. This is typical of Gainsborough's creative process in that the final composition has taken form from a previous idea rather than being slavishly copied from an earlier drawing or study.

The early history of this landscape is unknown as Gainsborough seems to have sold few of his landscapes during his lifetime, but it is likely that his widow Margaret sold it to Joseph Smith, private secretary to William Pitt, who owned it by the time of the important Gainsborough exhibition at the British Institution in 1814. It then descended in the Smith family until 1889 when it was sold privately to Sir Edward Guinness, in whose family it remained until 1990.

24

ABRAHAM PETHER

1756–1812

An Idealised Landscape with Kirkstall Abbey

Oil painting on canvas
Size: 47 × 59½ inches
Signed and dated 1793

Collection: Private collection.

Exhibited: Probably, London, Royal Academy, 1794, No. 46.
(Morning, with a view of Kirkstall Abbey in Yorkshire).

Abraham Pether was born at Chichester into an artistic milieu which included his uncle, William Pether a celebrated engraver and the 'three brothers Smith', well-known landscape painters of the period. During his life-time Pether was to become well-known as a landscape painter, especially for his moonlit landscapes, although it is generally considered that his pictures depicting daylight conditions are the most accomplished of his works. Pether was admired by many of his fellow artists, chief amongst them, Sir Thomas Lawrence. However, painting was only one of his many interests which amongst them numbered music, astronomy, microscopy and electricity, for all of which he constructed the appropriate instruments with his own hands.

Pether generally painted on a small, or very small, scale; with some of his pictures only measuring 3 by 4 inches. However, the present work is one of his largest and most ambitious canvases and it demonstrates Pether's great accomplishments as a landscape painter. At this period Pether seems to have been working in a particularly assured manner, which may owe something to a study of the work of Richard Wilson. Certainly his treatment of the foliage and the bold handling of the rocks in the foreground combined with a rather painterly interest in the construction of this picture belies interest in the major works of the best English and Irish painters of the mid

Eighteenth Century, rather than the Seventeenth Century Dutch painters of 'cabinet' pictures who were the usual influences in his smaller pictures. The last digit of the date is somewhat indistinct, but appears to be 3, and it is tempting because of the scale and obvious importance of this work, to associate it with Pether's Royal Academy exhibit of 1794.

The present picture is particularly interesting in belonging to that small group of British landscapes of the Eighteenth Century which include well-known buildings of picturesque antiquarian interest within the context of an idealised, and usually Italianate landscape. This served a dual purpose in not only *'elevating'* the subject of the picture by including it in a landscape which was a classic, if not a classical one in Claudean terms (much in the same way as Reynolds treated his sitters), but which was also intended to appeal to the prejudices of late eighteenth century English collectors who were usually uninterested in acquiring works by native artists in the face of a ready supply of genuine (or otherwise) Old Masters in the manner of Claude or Dughet; the most admired and collected of landscape masters amongst connoisseurs of the period.

fig. 53
Abraham Pether
Moonlight landscape
Oil painting on canvas
24 × 29 inches
National Trust, Anglesey Abbey
(Fairhaven collection)

25

JOSEPH MALLORD WILLIAM TURNER, R.A.

1775–1851

Finchley Church

Watercolour
$9\frac{1}{2} \times 12\frac{1}{8}$ inches
Inscribed on the reverse of the original mount *'Original drawing by Turner of Finchley Church made for my father in 1793 or 4 – Charles Monro'*.

Collections: Dr. Thomas Monro, commissioned from the artist;
Dr. Charles Monro, son of the above;
Mrs. Stotherd, by 1887;
Lady Howard-Dobson and R.A. Mills, 1979;
Private collection, 1993.

Exhibited: London, Royal Academy, *'Old Masters and Deceased Masters of the British School, including a Collection of Water-Colour Drawings by Joseph M.W. Turner, R.A.'*, Winter Exhibition, 1887, no. 14;
Kobe, The Museum of Modern Art; Iwate, Prefectural Museum; Saitama, The Museum of Modern Art; Hiroshima, Prefectural Museum; Kitakyushu, Municipal Museum of Art, *'The Rediscovery of Nature: An Anthology of 19th Century Landscape Painting in the West,'* 1983–4.

Literature: Sir Walter Armstrong, *'Turner'* 1902, p.253;
Andrew Wilton, *'The Life and Works of J.M.W. Turner, R.A.'*, 1979, p. 489, no. 40a, reproduced.

This exceptionally finely preserved watercolour of circa 1794 depicts the church of St. Mary at Finchley, a small village to the north of London (now part of Greater London). This work was made at the time that Turner was working for Dr. Thomas Monro, a prominent physician and a noted collector of contemporary British watercolours. At his London house in the Adelphi Dr. Monro ran what amounted to an informal 'academy', where young artists were encouraged by the Doctor paying them to make copies of watercolours for his collection. Monro was especially interested in the work of Thomas Hearne by whom he owned some three hundred watercolours and that of John Robert Cozens, his patient, to whose work he had access.

Turner stated that he had spent about three years at Monro's 'academy' which met in the evening and although it is not documented, the period between 1793 and 1795 would seem to be the likely dates of Turner's close involvement with Dr. Monro. This can be based not only on stylistic grounds but also on the evidence of commissioned works, such as the present watercolour and Monro's purchase at the Royal Academy in 1794 of Turner's *'St. Anselm's Chapel, Canterbury Cathedral'* (Whitworth Art Gallery, Manchester).

Monro also had a house at Bushey in Hertfordshire where both Turner and Girtin, amongst a number of artists including Hearne and Edridge, would visit him. His brother James lived nearby at Monken Hadley and a view showing St. Mary's Church, Monken Hadley and James Monro's house exists in two autograph versions (1) watercolour: Monro Family collection; (2) blue and grey washes: Private collection. The present watercolour depicts St. Mary's Church at Finchley where another of Dr. Monro's brothers lived. According to family

tradition (recorded in the catalogue of the 1887 Royal Academy Exhibition) Turner and Girtin would stop at Mr. Monro's house at Finchley for lunch on their way to the Doctor's house at Bushey. Members of the Whichcote family of nearby Hendon Hall (see no. 1) were buried in the church.

The present watercolour can be firmly dated to 1794, especially when compared with the two Monken Hadley views of 1793 (figs. 54 & 55) which display a Malton-like treatment of the architectural composition in common with other works of 1792–3. The documented works of 1794 show a more picturesque treatment of the whole composition combined with a more naturalistic handling of foliage and a bolder sophisticated use of a limited palette. Other comparable examples of 1794 include 'Arch of the Old Abbey at Evesham (fig. 56, Museum of Art, Rhode Island School of Design); The Porch of Great Malvern Abbey (fig. 57, Whitworth Art Gallery, Manchester); Christ Church, Oxford (fig. 58, Fitzwilliam Museum, Cambridge) and St. Anselm's Chapel, Canterbury Cathedral (Whitworth Art Gallery, Manchester, and purchased by Dr. Monro at the Royal Academy in 1794). The present work is especially notable in that it is a rare survival in unfaded condition demonstrating not only beautifully modulated lighting effects, but also a new strength of tonality which marks Turner's debut as a mature professional artist.

fig. 54
J.M.W. Turner
St. Mary's, Hadley
Watercolour
10½ × 14 inches
Signed and dated 1793
Private collection

fig. 55
J.M.W. Turner
St. Mary's, Hadley
Watercolour
11¼ × 14½ inches
Signed, inscribed 'sketch'
and dated August 19 1793
Private collection

fig. 56
J.M.W. Turner
Arch of the old Abbey, Evesham
Watercolour
$8\frac{1}{2} \times 10\frac{3}{8}$ inches
Signed and dated 1793
Museum of Art, Rhode Island
School of Design

fig. 57
J.M.W. Turner
St Anslem's Chapel
Watercolour
$20\frac{3}{8} \times 14\frac{3}{4}$ inches
Whitworth Art Gallery, Manchester

fig. 58
J.M.W. Turner
Christchurch, Oxford
Watercolour
Signed and dated 1794
Fitzwilliam Museum, Cambridge

26

JOSEPH MALLORD WILLIAM TURNER, R.A.

1775–1851

Sky and Sea

A Colour Beginning depicting a turbulent
Sky and Sea with a Sailing Vessel riding the Storm
in the middle-distance.

Watercolour
Size: 8⅞ × 12¼ inches
Bears collectors mark (Lugt 1517)
Painted in the mid-1820s

Collections: John Rutson (Lugt 1517), Nunnington Hall,
probably acquired in the 1850s or 1860s;
and by descent to 1993.

This powerful study dates from the mid 1820s, a period when Turner was gathering material for his *'Ports of England'* series of watercolours as well as working on the mezzotint plates of his unpublished *'Little Liber'* prints. Turner, from his earliest maturity as an artist, had had a fascination with the sea and many of the most important pictures throughout his career treated the theme of man's struggle against the elements at sea. The combination of this recurrent subject and Turner's great, and almost scientific, interest in atmospheric effects resulted in some of his most powerful colour studies which, unlike Constable's sky studies of the same period, have a strong romantic bias.

During the mid 1820s Turner (then in his late 40s) went through a period of particularly vigorous artistic self examination, which resulted in his exploration of the effects of light and sky in a small number of highly personal mezzotints (now known as the *'Little Liber'* series) which evidently were never intended for public circulation. These extraordinary prints, worked entirely by the artist himself are amongst his most

fig. 59
J.M.W. Turner
Ship in a storm
Watercolour
8½ × 11⅜ inches
Inscribed: *1, 2, 3, 4, 5*
The Turner Collection,
Tate Gallery
(T.B. CCLXIII – 309a)

personal and intense works of the period. There are a number of *'colour beginnings'* related to the *'Little Liber'* prints, and although the present work is not directly associated with any of the compositions it is closely related to both the subject matter of the prints and the treatment of their surviving preparatory studies.

The present colour beginning of sky and sea is a particularly complete and dramatic statement of the central theme in Turner's art: that of man's small place in his universe. The ship, however vital to the overall effect of the study, is merely suggested in pencil whilst the storm reflected or echoed in the sea is treated in Turner's most brilliant laying-in of free but highly controlled colour washes. *'Sky and Sea'* is one of the most beautiful and powerful of Turner's colour studies of this period and demonstrates not only his incomparable mastery of watercolour but his profound interpretation of nature.

27

JOSEPH MALLORD WILLIAM TURNER, R.A.

1775–1851

Oberwesel

Harvesters Resting on the slope above the Town, with
distant steamers on the Rhine.

Watercolour
Size: $13\frac{5}{8} \times 21$ inches
Signed and dated 1840

Collections: Benjamin Godfrey Windus;
Oldham Collection;
Whitaker Collection;
John Leigh Clark, Liverpool, sale Christie's, 28th March 1868, lot 100 (Agnews 860 gns.);
J.E. Fordham by 1877;
William Quilter, sale Christie's, 18th May 1889, lot 102, (Vokins 1,020 gns.);
Edward Steinkopff, by 1902, sale Christie's, 24th May 1935, lot 54, (Mitchell);
Lady Seaforth;
Dr. Marc Fitch, C.B.E.;
Private collection, 1994.

Literature: Sir Walter Armstrong, *'Turner'*, 1902, p. 269, repr. p. 124;
Andrew Wilton, *'The Life and Work of J.M.W. Turner'*, 1979, pp. 229–231, 465, no. 1380, repr. pl. 243;
Cecilia Powell, *'Turner's Rivers of Europe: The Rhine, Meuse and Mosel'*, 1991, pp. 20, 53, 54, 70, 118.

Exhibited: London, Royal Academy, *'Old Masters'*, 1873, no. 404;
Nottingham, Castle Museum, June 1878, no. 37;
London, Grosvenor Gallery, 1878, no. 6, (lent by W. Quilter);

(Exhibited cont.) London, Royal Academy, *'Old Masters . . . and a Collection of Watercolour Drawings by Joseph M.W. Turner, R.A.'*, 1889, no. 6;
London, Guildhall, 1899, no. 155;
London, The Leger Galleries, *'English Watercolours'*, 1972, no. 45, reproduced;
London, The Royal Academy, *'Turner 1775–1851'*, 1974–5, no. 583, reproduced;
London, The Leger Galleries, *'The Fitch Collection: The Major English Watercolours and Drawings Collected by Dr. Marc Fitch'*, 1988, no. 45, repr. in colour;
London, The Tate Gallery; Brussels, Musee d'Ixelles; and Bonn, Rheinishes Landesmuseum, *'Turners Rivers of Europe: The Rhine, Meuse and Mosel'*, September 1991–July 1992, no. 30, repr. in colour;
London, The Royal Academy, and Washington D.C., The National Gallery of Art, *'The Great Age of British Watercolours'*, 1993, no. 297, reproduced in colour.

This major watercolour is characterised by its *'surface sparkle'* and has been described by Cecilia Powell (op. cit.) as *'a masterpiece among Turner's late watercolours and it enshrines his most recent experiences in the Rhineland. It is in short, the final consummation of his long love of the Rhine and is his greatest painting of the greatest river of Europe'.*

There are a number of drawings of Oberwesel in the *'Treves to Cochem'* sketchbook of 1834 (T.B. CCXC), and in the *'Brussels to Mannheim'* sketchbook of circa 1840 (T.B. CCXVI), but none of these seems to correspond with the subject of the present watercolour, although it is quite possible that Ruskin may have destroyed a slight 'on the spot' sketch of this view when he was preparing the drawings in the Turner bequest for public view. However, it is almost certain that this watercolour was inspired by Turner's tour along the Meuse and Mosel in 1839 when he had made a point of taking views from high viewpoints and it is probable that Turner relied on his own memory, since the topographical nature of this watercolour was not a primary consideration as it had been in his earlier *'Picturesque'* views. Cecilia Powell has further noted that *'This dazzling vision of the Rhine . . . is not only the culmination of Turner's many visits to this part of Europe, but one of the most outstanding of all his late watercolours'.*

The importance of this particular watercolour, which should be compared with watercolours of *'Lake Nemi'* and *'Tancaville'* (British Museum, Lloyd Bequest), is that it forms a link between the *'England and Wales'* watercolours and the late Swiss and Venetian subjects, as well as being the final essay in the Claudean formula which in *'Oberwesel'* Turner has expanded to a definitive treatment of the 'Italianate' theme which had dominated European landscape painting for the previous two centuries.

'Oberwesel' is the key work in a group of six Swiss views, painted circa 1840, which mark the logical culmination of the great series of English and Continental watercolours of the 1820s and 1830s. Thereafter, Turner was to paint in a less formalised way, which was, incidentally, to be less acceptable to some of his patrons of the day.

Turner seems to have preferred, even from the early years of his career to work on series of related watercolours. This discipline, which allowed him to fully expand an idea, possibly originated with the groups of specifically topographical works which he made for the Earl of Essex, Sir Richard Colt Hoare, the Lascelles family and William Beckford before 1800. After his first visit to the Continent in 1802 he was fortunate in having patrons such as Fawkes, Munro of Novar and Windus, who were happy to acquire large groups of related drawings. In addition his early

sporadic work for publishers had increased, and from 1811, when he started work on *'Picturesque Views on the Southern Coast of Britain'* for W. B. Cook, he was constantly engaged in the preparation of large series of watercolours for publishers until about 1835. After that time he produced few pictures specifically for engraving, preferring to paint small groups of highly worked watercolours which he viewed as an end in themselves.

Benjamin Godfrey Windus (1790–1867), a member of a wealthy family of coach builders, made his first purchase of a watercolour by Turner in 1822. Like many nineteenth-century collectors he preferred to devote himself to the work of contemporary British artists although, unusually, he concentrated his attentions on the works of the watercolourists, which by the 1820s had developed into a vigorous and easily identifiable school.

By the late 1830s Windus had accumulated at his house at Tottenham a collection of some two hundred works by Turner including thirty six (over a third) of the England and Wales watercolours. Windus also owned the present drawing's companion, *'Lake Nemi'* (British Museum), which was also engraved in 1842, and the watercolour *'Zurich, fete, early morning'* (Kunsthaus, Zurich, formerly Leger Galleries). In 1835 Windus commissioned John Scarlett Davis to paint a view of the Library at Tottenham (British Museum) and this watercolour is the best record of what an important nineteenth-century collection of Turner's finished works looked like. Windus seems to have genuinely preferred to purchase his pictures through dealers, the most notable of whom was Thomas Griffith, rather than deal directly with the artist.

fig. 60
J.M.W. Turner
Oberwesel
Watercolour
$8\frac{11}{16} \times 14\frac{1}{4}$ inches
Painted in 1817
Formerly: Leger Galleries

fig. 62
John Scarlett Davis
B.G. Windus' Library
Watercolour
$11\frac{1}{2} \times 22$ inches
British Museum

fig. 61
J.M.W. Turner
Lake Nemi
Watercolour
$13\frac{3}{4} \times 20\frac{1}{2}$ inches
British Museum
(Lloyd Bequest)

JOHN LINNELL

1792–1882

Kensington Gardens

Watercolour
Size: 4 × 5½ inches
Signed, inscribed *'Kensington Gardens about 1812'*, and dated 1812 and numbered *'No. 1'*

Collections: The artist;
and by family descent to;
Joan Linnell Ivimy, 1993.

Exhibited: London, Royal Academy, *'Winter Exhibition of Works by Old Masters and by the Late John Linnell,'* 1883, no. 143;
London, P & D Colnaghi, *'A Loan Exhibition of Drawings, Watercolours and Paintings by John Linnell and his Circle'*, 1973, no. 19c;
London, Tate Gallery, *'Landscape in Britain 1750–1850'*, 1973–4, no. 244;
Hamburg, Kunsthalle, *'William Turner und die Landschaft seiner Zeit'*, 1976, no. 277;
Salisbury, The City Library, Salisbury Festival Exhibition, *'John Linnell 1792–1882'.* 1977, no. 17;
New York, Museum of Modern Art, *'Before Photography: Painting and the Invention of Photography'*, 1981, no. 30, repr. pp. 56–7;
Cambridge, Fitzwilliam Museum and New Haven, Yale Center for British Art, *'John Linnell: A Centennial Exhibition'*, 1982–3, no. 21.

Literature: J.L. Roget, *'A History of the 'Old Water-Colour' Society'*, 1891, Vol. I, p. 375.

The present work is one of the most beautiful watercolours of the early years of the nineteenth century and represents, to borrow the words of the organisers of the recent watercolour exhibition seen at the Royal Academy and the National Gallery of Art, Washington, *'an almost spiritual intensity most readily explained by Linnell's new understanding of landscape and its meticulous organisation as direct proof of God's existence. . . . These studies Linnell made in Bayswater also show a new interest in unassuming and often featureless slices of Nature, a far cry from the distinctly 'Picturesque' motifs of broken fences and gnarled trees he had sketched from nature in oil...only five years earlier'.* (Andrew Wilton and Anne Lyles, *'The Great Age of British Watercolours 1750–1880'*, p. 134).

The present watercolour belongs to a very small group of similarly-sized finished watercolours which obviously originally came from a sketchbook and it seems likely, from a knowledge of Linnell's predilection for working *'en plein air'* derived from his early studies with John Varley and latterly with Cornelius Varley, that he drew and painted directly onto the present sheet without the aid of any other preparatory material. It is possible to trace the inspiration for these extraordinary landscapes from the years of Linnell's training at the Royal Academy Schools where he was taught to study Classical art and he subsequently applied the same principle to landscape painting, by copying from nature directly as had the Greek sculptors when carving the Elgin Marbles.

In the years between about 1805 and 1810 Linnell was greatly influenced by the 'Picturesque' and his studies at the informal 'Academy' of Dr. Thomas Monro introduced him to the work of

Girtin, Gainsborough, Hearne and Cozens. Indeed Linnell and his friend and fellow artist William Mulready, also a student at the Royal Academy Schools, followed Gainsborough's example by setting-up small still-life models of landscapes which were carefully chosen picturesque specimens and '. . . *through the practice of very carefully copying all the beautiful varieties of tint and texture . . . we learnt to see beauty in everything*'. Linnell and Mulready at this period also experimented by painting outdoors in oil, as did William Henry Hunt, a fellow student at the Monro 'Academy'.

It was, however, Linnell's religious conversion in 1811 that gave rise to a powerful incentive for outdoor naturalism as a solution to his previously unresolved search for an artistic 'voice'. Although, nominally an Anglican, through the mediation of Cornelius Varley, Linnell was led into the Baptist community and his beliefs were firmly influenced by William Paley's '*Natural Theology*' which led him to understand landscape and the meticulous organisation of its proof of God's existence. 'Truth to Nature' became very much more than a style or an aesthetic; since nature was God's creation, the artistic act of witness could only take the form of accurate description. Accuracy, therefore, became a moral obligation.

In the period between 1809 and 1811 Linnell divided his time between living at his father's house at Streatham Street, Bloomsbury, and William Mulready's house by the Kensington gravel pits. However, in 1811 he took a second floor lodging at 11 Queen Street, Edgware Road, at a rent of £20 a year, and this address was used for his entries to the British Institution in 1811 and 1812.

The present work is perhaps the most beautiful of all Linnell's small Bayswater watercolours of 1811–12 and is especially notable for its pristine state of preservation. In its intensity of observation the present landscape anticipates, not only the work of Samuel Palmer, a protegée and eventual son-in-law, but also the landscapes of the Pre-Raphaelite painters who also sought after *'truth to nature'*.

fig. 63
John Linnell
Kensington Gravel Pits
Oil painting on canvas
27 × 41 inches
Tate Gallery

fig. 64
John Linnell
A view from the Edgeware Road
Oil painting on board
14½ × 15¼ inches
Inscribed and dated 1812
Royal Borough of Kensington and Chelsea
Leighton House

fig. 65
John Linnell
Corn Harvest, Bayswater
Watercolour
4 × 5¾ inches
Signed and dated *'1811 or 1814'*
Private collection

fig. 66
John Linnell
The foundations of Stratten's Chapel
Watercolour
4 × 5¾ inches
Signed and dated 1811
Yale Center for British Art (Mellon collection)

29

GEORGE FENNEL ROBSON

1788–1833

Stirling Castle

Watercolour
Size: $26\frac{1}{4} \times 32\frac{3}{4}$ inches
Painted circa 1820

Collections: The Earls of Dalhousie, Panmure House, to 1993.

George Fennel Robson was born at Durham, the eldest son of a wine merchant, and it is recorded that in his early years he became fascinated by the many artists, who when visiting the city, sketched in the open. After making copies of Bewick's woodcuts and receiving some local instruction in drawing , he set off to London with a loan of five pounds from his father. In 1807, at the age of nineteen, Robson exhibited a view on the River Tees at the Royal Academy and after the successful publication of a print of his home town was able to return his father's money and pay a prolonged visit to Scotland, where dressed, according to one source, *'as a shepherd, and with his wallet at his back, and Scott's 'Lay of the Last Minstrel' in his pocket, he wandered over the mountains'*. The success of his Scottish subjects ensured his election as a member of the Associated Artists in 1810 and on its break-up he was elected to the Old Water-Colour Society in 1813 which was followed by the publication of his *'Scenery of the Grampian Mountains'* containing forty soft-ground etchings.

Robson was a prolific exhibitor at the O.W.C.S., of which he was elected President in 1820. The majority of the pictures were Scottish subjects which achieved prices as high as seventy five guineas and purchasers including Walter Fawkes; Lord Suffield; Thomas Griffiths; Robert Peel; John Allnutt; Benjamin Windus; and George Haldimand, for whose wife Robson assembled a famous album of watercolours by all the leading artists of the period. His watercolours met with considerable critical, as well

fig. 67
Edward Finden
(after G.F. Robson)
Stirling Castle
Engraving
Published 1832

as commercial, success, being praised for their *depth of repose,* their *largeness and illusive reality* as well as for their *natural gradations* and *luminous skies.* John Ruskin was an admirer of Robson's works (with certain reservations) and noted in *'Modern Painters'* that his landscapes were *'serious and quiet in the highest degree; certain qualities of atmosphere and texture in them have never been excelled, and certain facts of mountain scenery never but by them expressed; as, for instance, the stillness and depth of the mountain tarns, with the reversed imagery of their darkness signed by the soft lines of faintly touching winds; the solemn flush of the brown fern and glowing heath under evening light; the purple mass of mountains far removed, seen against clear still twilight'. (Modern Painters, 1888, Vol. I, p.94).*

Stirling Castle and its precipitous position was a dramatic subject which was to appeal to Robson who exhibited seven compositions of Stirling between 1815 and 1830, with an engraving being made of one of them in 1823, (fig. 67). The present picture contained within its original frame has all the hallmarks of an exhibition piece although it is now impossible to know if and when it appeared at the O.W.C.S. although in 1821 Thomas Griffiths, Turner's dealer, purchased a view of Sterling for thirty five guineas and in 1830 another composition was priced at forty five guineas, both figures being commensurate with the size and importance of the present work.

30

GEORGE BARRET JNR.

1767–1842

An Arcadian Landscape at Sunset with a Shepherd
and his Flock in the Foreground

Watercolour
Size: 10³⁄₁₆ × 8⁹⁄₁₆ inches
Signed and dated 1830

Collections: Henry Vaughan;
John Lewis Roget;
and by descent to 1993.

Exhibited: London, Burlington Fine Arts Club, *'English Water-Colours'*, 1871;
London, Royal Academy, *'Winter Loan Exhibition'*, 1908.

fig. 68
George Barret Jnr.
Classical landscape
Watercolour
Signed and dated 1840
Birmingham Museums and Art Gallery

In 1804 George Barret, the son of one of the founder members of the Royal Academy (see nos. 21 & 22), became one of the founder members of the Society of Painters in Water-Colours, or the O.W.C.S. as it was to become known. Barret had exhibited his first watercolour in 1800 and even at that early stage he appears to have been fascinated by the qualities of morning and evening lighting effects. John Lewis Roget, an early owner of this particular watercolour and the historian of the Old Water-Colour Society records that Barret *'used to say that he gained more by studying in the early morning and the evening than at any other time. His habit was to go to the same spot and watch the sunrise, morning after morning, making slight memoranda. He used to wait until the effect appeared that suited him, and go to the same sketch over and over again at the same hour on different days, working only as long as the particular effect lasted, under which he had commenced his study. This mode of practice he continued through life, and the titles of his works show how long and fondly he adhered to his favourite aspect of nature'* (J.L. Roget, A' *History of the Old Water-Colour Society'* 1891, Vol. I, p.177).

Barret was disinterested in topography and the majority of the very large number of his exhibited works were not of specific locations, but had evocative descriptive titles which included *'Morning'*, *'Evening'*, *'Sunset'*, *'Twilight'*, *'Composition'* and those such as *'Solitude'*. Barret's works of this period were noted by his contemporaries for their *'depth, richness, and luxuriance of contour'* and also that they were *'so faithful to nature, and compatible with the magnificent scenery which he delights to design, has grown inperceptibly from practice, which, developing from year to year new powers in the material in which he works, is thus displayed in pictures that combine all the higher excellences of the renowned Italian school, and yet are purely original'* (W.H. Pyne, *'The rise and progress of water-colour painting in England'* Somerset House Gazette, 1822–2, II, p.47).

31

PAUL SANDBY MUNN

1773–1845

The Mill at Ambleside

Watercolour
Size: $7\frac{7}{8} \times 6\frac{1}{8}$ inches
Signed and dated 1833

The artist's father, James Munn, a carriage decorator and landscape painter at Greenwich, was a friend of Paul Sandby, who became godfather to Paul Sandby Munn. Sandby gave early lessons to his godson who progressed to the extent that in 1799 he was able to exhibit landscapes at the Royal Academy, as well as becoming a member of Girtin's Sketching Club of which he would later become secretary. His two brothers had a stationery and printsellers shop at 107 New Bond Street, and Munn was based at these premises making watercolours which were purchased in the shop by young ladies as drawing copies; indeed, such was the demand that Munn solicited the help of his friend Cotman in maintaining the supply of these landscape watercolours. This was in fact Cotman's main employment during the years between 1802 and 1804 and the two artists made sketching tours to North Wales in 1802 and Yorkshire in 1803. Munn does not appear to have been especially ambitious as a painter and he ceased to exhibit after 1815, at which point he probably settled at Hastings where he established himself as a drawing-master.

Munn exhibited forty watercolours at the Old Water Colour Society between 1806 and 1815 and he appears to have particularly favoured the scenery of the Lake District, exhibiting views of Crummock Water, Coniston, Troutbeck and various views of Ambleside including a *Mill at Ambleside* in 1812. A larger variant of the present composition dated 1815 is in a private collection.

In the earlier part of his career Munn favoured the type of 'stained drawing' about which, no doubt, he had taught both by Sandby and by his father. Although he became more fully chromatic in his use of the medium as in the present example, his pigments have usually proved to be extremely prone to fading and it is rare, as in this watercolour, to find his work displaying a full use of the palette.

fig. 69
Paul Sandby Munn
Cottages in Westmorland
Watercolour
$13\frac{7}{8} \times 21\frac{3}{4}$ inches
Signed and dated 1807
Cecil Higgins Art Gallery,
Bedford

32

JOHN CONSTABLE, R.A.

1776–1837

An Important Double-Sided Sheet of Cloud Studies

Cloud Study (recto)
Sky and Sea (verso)

Watercolour
Size: $4\frac{1}{4} \times 6\frac{3}{4}$ inches (11×17.5 cm)
Painted in the early 1830s

Collections: Lord de Ramsey, 1993

Literature: To be included by Graham Reynolds in any supplement or second edition of *'The Later Paintings and Drawings of John Constable'*

This exceptional double-sided watercolour study dates from the early 1830s and demonstrates Constable's continuing fascination with both the scientific and emotional aspects of landscape painting. This sheet is notable not only for its extraordinary condition but also in its demonstration of Constable's great technical facility in capturing fleeting cloud formations and shifting lighting effects. This is especially evident in the study of Sky and Sea (verso) in which Constable deftly captures the effects of light and shadow falling on the gently rolling water.

Constable had his first serious bout of *'Skying'* in 1821 when he wrote that *'I have done a good deal of skying – I am determined to conquer all difficulties and that most arduous one among the rest. . . . That Landscape painter who does not make his skies a very material part of the composition – neglects to avail himself of one of his greatest aids. Sir Joshua Reynolds speaking of the 'landscape' of Titian & Salvator & Claude – says 'Even their skies seem to sympathise with the subject'. I have often been advised to consider my sky – as a 'white sheet drawn behind the objects'. Certainly if the sky is obtrusive (as mine are)*

it is bad, but if they are evaded (as mine are not) it is worse, they must and always shall with me make an effectual part of the composition. It will be difficult to name a class of Landscape, in which the sky is not the 'key note', the standard of 'Scale', and a chief 'Organ of sentiment'. You may conceive then what a 'white sheet' would do for me, impressed as I am with these notions, and they cannot be Erroneous. The sky is the 'source of light' in nature – and governs everything. Even our common observations on the weather of every day, are suggested by them but it does not occur to us. Their difficulty in painting both as to composition and execution is very great, because with all their brilliancy and consequence, they ought not to come forward or be hardly thought about in a picture – any more than extreme distances are'. (John Constable to John Fisher, 23 September, 1821). It was at this period that Constable sustained his most intensive bout of *skying*, systematically noting the prevailing weather conditions on the reverse of his studies, which at this point were largely executed in oils.

It was possibly during his visit to Sir George and Lady Beaumont at Coleorton in the autumn of 1823, that Constable made pencil copies of the twenty engravings of different types of skies which formed the central part of Alexander Cozens's *'New Method'* (Courtauld Institute Galleries). In addition Bishop Fisher introduced him to Gilbert White's *'Natural History of Selbourne'* telling the artist that *'it is in your own way of close natural observation'.* Constable's interest in the comparatively new science of meteorology is further evidenced by his annotated copy of Thomas Forster's 1815 edition of *'Researches about Atmospheric Phaenomena'*, which set out, following the example of Luke Howard in his *'The Climate of London'* (1820), to classify the types of clouds by the names that they are still known.

In the early 1830s he again returned to making studies in both oils and watercolours of clouds and this emphasised his strongly held belief that climate was not merely an adjunct of landscape but *the chief organ of sentiment*. By the 1830s Constable's interest in transient effects had become extremely complex and this may have been the result, as Malcolm Cormack has recently pointed out, of his constant work on the proofs of David Lucas' mezzotints for *English Landscape Scenery* which probably developed his already very great interest in light and shade. In his description to the plate of *Spring* (fig. 70) Constable wrote that he hoped that the print would *give some idea of one of those bright and animated days of the early year, when all nature bears so exhilarating an aspect…causing that playful change so much desired by the painter of*

> *Light and shade alternate, warmth and cold,*
> *And bright and dewy clouds, and vernal show'rs,*
> *And all the fine variety of things . . .'*

Constable's cloud studies are notable because they are emotional responses to nature rather than strictly scientific studies or copies of nature, and in this respect he was very much a man of his age and his sensibilities ran parallel to those of the romantic poets who also found nature matching man's emotions as in Shelley's *Ode to the West Wind*:

> *Thou on whose stream, mid the steep sky's commotion.*
> *Loose clouds like earth's decaying leaves are shed,*
> *Shook from the tangled boughs of heaven and ocean . . .*

However, Constable was to make the point in a lecture at the Royal Institution in 1836 that *We see nothing truly till we understand it*, and the intense studies that he made of natural effects confirm the importance that he attached to them, especially as it is interesting to note that unlike his other studies from nature, Constable never appears to have used any of his numerous cloud studies, in either oil or watercolour, directly in his finished pictures, but the knowledge derived from their execution enabled the artist to improvise, appropriately moody, yet convincing skies in the studio.

Constable's sky studies are notoriously difficult to date accurately, as individual cloud studies were made from about 1806 onwards, but they tend to fall into two main groups, made in the early 1820s, from 1821, and in the early 1830s. Jane McAusland had pointed out that the present sheet is executed on a Whatman paper, which although undated, is similar to those used for other studies made in the early 1830s.

fig. 70
David Lucas (after Constable)
Spring
Mezzotint

fig. 71
John Constable
London from Hampstead Heath
Watercolour
$4\frac{5}{16} \times 7\frac{1}{4}$ inches
British Museum

fig. 72
John Constable
Cloud study
Watercolour
Musée du Louvre, Paris

33

JAMES HOLLAND O.W.S.

1800–1870

An Extensive Open Landscape at Dawn with a Range of Mountains in the Distance

Watercolour
Size: 10 × 19½ inches
Painted circa 1837

fig. 73
James Holland
Sunset over an estuary
Watercolour
9½ × 5¼ inches
Henry E Huntington Library
and Art Gallery, San Marino

Collections: James Holland, the artist, sale of the remaining contents of his studio, Christie's, 26–27th May, 1870, (possibly lot 317, *'Cintra 1837'*, 8 gns to E. White);
Sir Henry Houldsworth Bt., 1949;
Private collection, 1993.

Literature: Frank Davis, *'A James Holland Exhibition'*, The Illustrated London News, May 21, 1949, p. 710, reproduced.

Exhibited: London, The Leger Galleries, *'Watercolours and Sketches by James Holland'*, 1949, no. 2.

James Holland came from a family of Staffordshire designers and painters of pottery, and it was in this branch of the arts that he received his earliest training, specialising as a painter of flowers on ceramics. He moved to London in 1819 and gave drawing lessons as well as supporting himself by producing small watercolours of flowers, suitable for ladies' albums, which survive in some quantities. In 1831 he visited France for the first time and whilst there he was strongly influenced by the work of Bonington and his circle.

The watercolours of the 1830s, and especially those deriving from his visit to Portugal in 1837, are amongst the most beautiful of his works. After about 1845 his work became over-finished and elaborate, loosing the fluency of handling of the colour washes and the underdrawing which marks, both the finished 'studio' watercolours and his 'on the spot' sketches of the 1830s as being amongst the most advanced and beautiful watercolours of the period.

The present *'plein air'* study almost certainly dates from Holland's visit to Portugal in 1837 when he made some of his most dashing studies. Although this study has lost its original identification it would appear to depict the scenery around Cintra. This work was one of a large group of watercolours purchased at the artist's posthumous sale at Christie's in 1870 by E. White which by 1949 had found their way into the collection of a Scottish baronet, Sir Henry Houldsworth, from whom they were acquired by the Leger Galleries. The collection was exhibited by Leger in a well publicised exhibition in 1949 and the present work, by then only identified as *'Clouds'*, was subsequently acquired by the collector with whom it remained until recently.

This study is notable, not only for the great beauty of the composition, but also for the artist's advanced and completely spontaneous response to nature and it should be judged alongside contemporary studies from nature made by other pioneers of romanticism, including Constable and Turner.

34

WILLIAM TURNER OF OXFORD

1789–1862

Boating on the Isis
A View of Oxford from the River Isis with sailing Vessels
in a stiff breeze

Watercolour
Size: 10⅛×15 inches
Painted in the late 1830s

Collections: Geoffrey Gilchrist Mure;
and by descent to 1993.

William Turner was born near Oxford, where he was to spend the greater part of his career. He demonstrated an early interest in drawing and in 1804 he was placed as a pupil (or possibly apprentice) to John Varley in London, at the same time that John Linnell (see no. 28) was also a pupil. Turner first exhibited at the Royal Academy in 1807 and in 1808 was elected to the Society of Painters in Water-Colours as its youngest member. It was at this time that Farington recorded that *"Varley spoke violently of the merit of a young man who has been his Pupil in learning to draw in watercolour and Reinagle said 'He had never before seen drawings equal to them'. His name is Turner".*

Turner of Oxford was a regular, but not prolific, exhibitor in London as he preferred to show only major highly finished works which represented his particular interest in creating landscapes which were carefully articulated artistic statements. The present picture which survives in the most remarkable state, exemplifies the best work of Turner's middle period, where unlike so many of his contemporaries he avoided any generalisation of detail or concept and instead relied on minute observation and an imposed order to create a memorable image. William Turner exhibited a number of watercolours of similar subjects and it is now impossible to ascertain whether this picture was one of them, although its quality certainly suggests that it was likely to have been exhibited at the Royal Society of Painters in Water-Colours.

Before college rowing became established in the 1820s, sailing was a popular undergraduate pastime and this stretch of the river to the south of the city was well known for its squally conditions.

fig. 74
William Turner of Oxford
On the Isis
Watercolour
9 × 14½ inches
Signed
Private collection

35

JAMES STARK

1794–1859

A View near Trowse, Norwich

Oil painting on panel.
Size: $22 \times 30\frac{1}{2}$ inches
Painted circa 1820

Collections: John Rushout, 2nd Baron Northwick, Northwick
Park, (d.1859);
George Rushout, 3rd Baron Northwick, nephew of
the above, (d.1887);
Elizabeth Augusta, Lady Northwick, widow of the
above, (d. 1912);
Edward George Spencer-Churchill, grandson of
the above, Northwick Park, 1965;
Private collection, 1993.

Literature: *'Catalogue of The Pictures at Northwick Park'*, 1864,
no. 82;
Dr. Tancred Borenius and Lionel Cust, *'Catalogue of
The Collection of Pictures at Northwick Park'*, 1921,
p.142, no. 377.

James Stark was born in Norwich; his father was a Scotsman who
had settled there, pursuing a successful trade as a dyer. Stark was
apparently not a strong child and whilst his elder brothers were
educated for their father's trade, he was sent to Norwich
Grammar School where he met John Berney Crome, the eldest
son of John Crome, then the leading artist in the Norwich area.
Stark's early ambition to pursue farming as a career came to
nothing, and through his intimacy with the Crome family he
appears to have become attracted to becoming a painter,
resulting in his apprenticeship to John Crome in 1811 for a
period of three years. It is likely that his indentures merely
formalised an existing master/pupil relationship, since James
Stark exhibited pictures both at the Norwich Exhibition and
the Royal Academy in 1811.

After his indenture expired in 1814 Stark was largely based in
London and by 1819 he was making a reputation as a landscape
painter and his Royal Academy exhibits of that year secured him
the patronage of collectors of considerable influence such as Sir
George Beaumont and Lord Northwick, the original owner of
the present work. Lord Northwick's great collection was mostly
hung at Thirlstaine House at Cheltenham, and comprised some
fifteen hundred works which were sold after his death in a sale
lasting twenty one days. However, the present picture appears to
have remained at Northwick Park, his other seat in Gloucester-
shire.

It was at about this time that Stark's health necessitated a return
to Norwich, where he was to remain living for the following
twelve years. This return to his roots and to the large and
essentially conservative East Anglian market for landscape
paintings, possibly largely prevented Stark from pursuing a
possibly more ambitious landscape style in favour of refining an
intimate landscape genre, beloved by the Norwich school of
painters, which essentially continued the tradition of the
seventeenth century Dutch painters who had been painting in
and operating under similar circumstances.

W.F. Dickes, the pioneering historian of the Norwich School,
characterised Stark's style as being *'thoroughly English, yet their
originality prevents comparison with the works of his contemporaries,*
whilst finding in them *unaffected realism.'* In what is still the
standard work, Dickes recorded that:

'Both his dark touches (generally Cologne earth), and his flake-white lights are pure, sharply defined, and often in sudden contrast. He frequently each of his various colours to assert itself – pure and untoned in some part or other of his picture. Variety was his aim, and this he succeeded in obtaining quite as often by the multiplicity of objects as by enrichment.

But perhaps another point distinguishing Stark among his contemporaries was his texture. This, as produced by his ever changing touch, is admirable. Thus he would adopt for his architecture a flat, square touch; an up and down or diagonal touch for his foreground, stubble, or grass; a drop-and-lift touch for his foliage, and a sweep for his distances. In his hand difference of texture would suffice to distinguish – say a stubbled cornfield from a rutted road, though both might be sienna in colour. In the same way he would scatter dead, shrivelled oak leaves upon the foreground by sharply dropping and lifting a well-loaded brush.

His trees, often elaborately branched and neatly foliaged, are built up with touches of light and dark colours in abrupt and sharp contrast. As to the choice of pigments for his skies, it may be observed that he was partial to a bright Naples yellow, and that the grey of his clouds is more neutral than that of Crome; he evidently admitted black into it'. (William Frederick Dickes, *'The Norwich School of Painting'*, 1905, pp. 491–2).

The meadows around Trowse, a small village on the outskirts of Norwich, were a particularly favoured spot by painters in the early nineteenth century.

fig. 75
James Stark
The Mill
Oil painting on canvas
Metropolitan Museum of Art, New York

fig. 76
James Stark
A lane near Norwich
Oil painting on canvas
22 × 30 inches
Fitzwilliam Museum, Cambridge

36

FREDERICK RICHARD LEE, R.A.

1798–1879

A Set of Five Views on the Lynedoch Estate near Perth

Oil on board
Size: 13¾ × 9⅞ inches
Signed, inscribed and dated 1839 on labels on the reverse of
four of the pictures

Collections: William and Elizabeth Whitbread;
                 W. Mills.

This set of five views on the Lynedoch estate near Perth depicts *'The New Bridge; The Saw Mills; The Swiss Bridge; The Summer House above the Swiss Bridge'* and a view of another now unidentified bridge on the River Almond. These charming views were painted for William and Elizabeth Whitbread and, according to the original inscribed labels, in their possession by October 1838.

Frederick Richard Lee was one of the most popular and successful landscape painters of his period. He was born in Barnstaple in Devon into a landowning family and as a young man served in the army as an Ensign in the 56th Foot, taking part in the ill-starred expedition to Bergen-op-Zoom in 1813 when the almost impregnable fortress was almost taken, under the command of Sir George Graham, later created Lord Lynedoch. However, after being invalided home, he resigned his commission on the grounds of ill health. Lee then decided to turn to art and by 1818 he was enrolled as a student at the Royal Academy Schools, first exhibiting at the British Institution in 1822 and at the Royal Academy two years later. Lee was elected a full Member of the Royal Academy in 1838, the year that the present pictures were painted.

Lee was, from the outset of his career, an extremely popular artist attracting the patronage of William Wells of Redleaf and Lord Northwick, two of the most important patrons of the period. Such was his professional progress that in 1838, on the vacancy caused by the death of John Constable who it appears was somewhat jealous of the younger artist's considerable commercial success, he was elected a full member of the Royal Academy. Lee was unusual amongst his fellow Academicians in being far more interested in shooting, fishing, yachting, photography and mechanics, whilst regarding his skill as a painter as a means of amassing a fortune and the wherewithal to follow his other interests. Although he had purchased a house at Penshurst in Kent, Lee inherited the beautiful family estate at Pilton, on Barnstable Bay, where he was to spend the majority of his time. As time went on he spent an increasing amount of time on his yacht, making long and arduous voyages, but still continued to maintain the quality and numbers of pictures which he sent to the annual exhibitions, belying his apparent indifference to his art.

The Lynedoch estate near Perth had been purchased in 1787 by George Graham of Balgowan, who had recently married Mary Cathcart, a great beauty, and the subject of one of Gainsborough's finest portraits. Graham, who was elevated to the peerage after the success of his command during the Peninsula War, as Baron Lynedoch, may have known the painter; however, the River Almond was noted at this time for its sport and this may have attracted the painter to this spot. William Whitbread who appears to have been the first owner of these pictures, may have commissioned them. A larger oil of the *'Old Bridge at Lynedoch over the River Almond'* was exhibited at the British Institution in 1839.

37

JOHN FERNELEY SNR.

1782–1860

The Manners Family Hunting Group

The 5th Duke of Rutland leading the field of the
Belvoir Hunt and closely followed by his eldest son
Lord Charles (Cecil John) Manners on the chestnut,
'Featherlegs', and his second son Lord (John James)
Robert Manners on the grey beyond, 'Benefit'; the family
seat Belvoir Castle is seen in the background.

Oil painting on unlined canvas
$35 \times 55\frac{1}{4}$ inches
Signed and dated 1838

Collections: Commissioned by Andrew Robert Drummond (1794–1865), son-in-law to the Duke of Rutland; and thence by family descent to 1993.

Literature: Major Guy Paget, *'The Melton Mowbray of John Ferneley, 1782–1860'*, 1931, reproduced opposite p. 110.

Exhibited: Leicester, Museum and Art Gallery, *'John Ferneley, 1782–1860'*, 1960, no. 36 (lent by M.A. Drummond).

The 1830s and 1840s are generally regarded as being the *'golden age'* of fox hunting and John Ferneley who established his studio in the hunting town of Melton Mowbray was the finest exponent of the hunting-piece. His sophisticated paintings, along with the prints of Alken, have become the definitive records of the period. The present group, one of Ferneley's most accomplished works, depicts the three senior members of the Manners family, amongst the wealthiest landed proprietors of the age, out with their celebrated pack of hounds.

Lord Charles (Cecil John) Manners (1815–1888) succeeded his father as 6th Duke: in turn he was succeeded by his brother Lord (John James) Robert Manners (1818–1906), as the former died unmarried.

The Duke of Rutland's hounds, known as the Belvoir Hunt, can be traced as far back as the seventeenth century, when the 1st Duke kept a substantial kennel at Belvoir Castle for hunting deer. By the late eighteenth century the pack was hunting the fox.

The 5th Duke, seen leading the field in the picture, was a great champion and patron of Ferneley. Ferneley, originally apprenticed to his father, a wheelwright, started his artistic career by making sketches of hunting scenes and copying prints as well as painting carts. It was apparently one of his decorated carts which brought the young Ferneley to the notice of the 5th Duke who arranged in 1801 for him to be apprenticed to Ben Marshall. In 1814 Ferneley moved to Elgin Lodge in Melton Mowbray, a town which attracted sportsmen hunting with the Belvoir and Quorn Hunts.

The present picture was commissioned by Andrew Drummond (1794–1865) who was married to the 5th Duke's daughter, Lady Elizabeth. Both he and his father, Andrew Berkeley Drummond (1755–1833) were keen sportsmen and patrons of Ferneley commissioning nine pictures over a fourteen year period between 1818 and 1831. This group which has descended in the Drummond family and which remains unlined and in pristine condition, demonstrates not only Ferneley's great virtuosity as a painter of horses but his elegant and lively sense of composition. It is as one would expect of a picture depicting and commissioned by the family of his great early patron, a work of the finest quality.

fig. 77
John Ferneley
The Belvoir Hounds leaving kennels
Oil painting on canvas
40 × 50 inches
Private collection

fig. 88
John Ferneley
The Raby Hunt
Oil painting on canvas
54 × 120 inches
Signed and dated 1828
Formerly: Leger Galleries

TERMS AND CONDITIONS OF SALE
(As adopted by The Society of London Art Dealers and registered in accordance with the Restrictive Trade Practices Act 1976)

RISK AND TITLE

1. Risk passes to the buyer on delivery. The buyer should therefore make appropriate arrangements fully to insure the work referred to.

2. The seller retains ownership of the work until the buyer has paid the purchase price in full.

PAYMENT

3. The price of the work, including delivery costs and any VAT that may be due, is to be paid in full without deduction at the time of delivery by cash or banker's draft or irrevocable letter of credit issued or confirmed by a bank acceptable to the seller unless another method of payment is agreed. If payment by cheque is accepted, that acceptance is conditional upon payment in full on first presentation.

4. Time for payment shall be of the essence of this Agreement. All sums paid late will bear interest to be computed on a daily basis at the rate of 3% per annum above Barclays Bank Base Rate for the time being in force for the period of delayed payment.

5. The buyer may not before payment in full of the price to the seller, except with the seller's prior written consent:
   (a) sell, export, dispose of, part with possession of, or otherwise deal with the work or attempt to do so; and
   (b) in the case of a work consisting of more than one item, separate those items.

6. The buyer shall be a bailee of the work for the seller until title has passed to the buyer and agrees that if in possession of the work before payment of the purchase price in full he will:
   (a) keep any identifying marks of the seller clearly displayed on the work;
   (b) store the work upon his premises separately from his own goods or those of any other person;
   (c) at the seller's request at all times allow the seller or his agent access thereto and facilities for inspection thereof; and
   (d) preserve the work in an unaltered state and in particular not undertake any work of restoration, repair, cleaning or reframing.

7. If the buyer fails to pay in full for the work in accordance with the agreement for sale and/or as provided for in paragraph 3 hereof or is in breach of paragraphs 5 or 6 or if at any time before payment in full an act or proceeding occurs or commences whether in the United Kingdom or elsewhere involving the buyer's solvency such as the presentation of a bankruptcy petition or winding up petition or the convening of a meeting to wind up voluntarily or application for an interim order for a voluntary arrangement or for the appointment of an administrator or the appointment of an administrative or other receiver or if the buyer does or fails to do anything which may in any way imperil the title of the seller to the work the seller may at any time thereafter repossess the work and/or avoid the sale with or without notice and the buyer agrees that for this purpose he will at the seller's request return the work to the seller at such address as the seller may nominate in London or at his option the seller may enter the premises where the work is kept and the buyer shall at the seller's request inform him of its whereabouts. Where the work consists of more than one item the right of repossession extends to all those items.

LIABILITY OF SELLER

8. The seller warrants that he has a right to sell the work.

9. The buyer and seller acknowledge that it is unreasonable that the seller should be subject to liability for an unlimited period of time and agree that all liability of the seller to the buyer and all rights of the buyer against the seller in relation to the work howsoever arising and of whatever nature shall cease after the expiry of six years from the date of delivery of the work to the buyer. This paragraph does not prejudice the buyer's statutory rights pursuant to Section 32 (1a) and (1b) of the Limitation Act 1980.

ARBITRATION

10. All claims, disputes and differences of whatsoever nature and whensoever arising in relation to, arising out of, or in connection with this Agreement, including but without prejudice to the generality of the foregoing those relating to the rights, liabilities or duties are to be referred to a single arbitrator who should be a Queen's Counsel practising at the Bar of England and Wales who should be chosen by agreement of the parties and in default of agreement within 28 days of a request by either of them to approve the appointment, by the Chairman for the time being of the Bar of England and Wales. The arbitration shall take place in London England and the award and the findings of the arbitrator shall be final and binding upon the parties. Any request pursuant to this paragraph shall be made in writing, sent by post to the principal place of business of the seller at the time of posting or to the last known address of the buyer, and shall be deemed to have been delivered on the third day after posting. For this purpose the date of commencement of the arbiration shall be as defined in Section 34 of the Limitation Act 1980.

11. Save that the buyer acknowledges the seller's right to seek, and the power of the High Court to grant interim relief namely, injunctions, Mareva and Anton Piller Orders, and Orders for the preservation, interim custody, detention or inspection of the work, no action shall be brought in relation to any dispute or difference referred to in paragraph 10 above, until the arbitrator appointed under paragraph 10 above has conducted an arbitration and made their award thereon.

PROPER LAW AND JURISDICTION

12. The proper law of this Agreement is English Law.

13. Insofar as any Court has jurisdiction, the parties irrevocably submit to the exclusive jurisdiction of the High Court of Justice of England and Wales over all matters arising out of or in connection with this Agreement.

EXPORT

14. Where the work which is the subject of this Agreement is to be exported from the United Kingdom by the buyer, this Agreement is conditional on the granting by the appropriate authorities of any requisite export licence, which the buyer shall use his best endeavours to obtain.

15. Where the work which is the subject of this Agreement is to be exported from the United Kingdom and Value Added Tax has not been charged because, by reason of such intended export, the work is zero rated or not subject to Value Added Tax, the buyer shall take all necessary steps to export the work within the time limits and in accordance with the formalities laid down by HM Customs and Excise and shall formally notify the Customs and Excise authorities of the said export and shall complete such documentation as they may require. The buyer shall idemnify the seller against any claims made against the seller for Value Added Tax or any other expenses or penalties by HM Customs and Excise by reason of the buyer's failure to observe the formalities referred to herein.

CARRIAGE

16. The buyer shall pay the cost of deliver and transit insurance of the work.

SET-OFF

17. The buyer shall not be entitled to the benefit of any set-off and sums payable to the seller shall be paid without any deduction whatsover. In the event of non-payment the seller shall be entitled to obtain and enforce judgement without determination of any cross claim by the buyer.

18. The benefit of this Agreement and any of the rights granted thereunder shall not be assignable by the buyer and shall rest solely and exclusively with the buyer.

19. Any notice pursuant to or in connection with this Agreement shall be in writing and shall be sent by post to the seller's principal place of business at the time of posting and in the case of the buyer to his last known address and shall be deemed to have been delivered on the third day after posting.

20. In the case of a consumer contract within the meaning of the Unfair Contract Terms Act 1977, these conditions shall not apply to the extent that they would be rendered void or unenforceable by virtue of the provisions thereof.

21. The conditions supersede any earlier terms contained in any documents emanating from the seller or any agents of the seller, and constitute the only terms upon which the seller is willing to sell the work. The buyer, by ordering or taking delivery of the work, agrees that they shall apply to the exclusion of his own conditions (if any).

22. No amendment, modification or waiver of any terms or conditions herein may be made, except in writing signed by the seller, or if the seller is a limited company by a director thereof.

23. In the event that the work which is the subject of this Agreement is to be insured by the gallery until collection or delivery, the liability of the gallery, following loss or damage to such work, shall be limited to the net selling price, notwithstanding that such loss and/or damage may have been caused or contributed to the negligence of the gallery, their Agents or Employees of both.

Designed and produced by Amadeus
Printed by Watmoughs (Fine Art) Printers, London and Bradford